Library of Pastoral Care

THE PASTORAL CARE OF THE DYING

The Library of Pastoral Care

TITLES ALREADY PUBLISHED

IN PREPARATION

Other volumes are planned

The
Pastoral Care of
The Dying

NORMAN AUTTON

Director of Training
Church Assembly Hospital Chaplaincies Council

LONDON
S·P·C·K
1969

First published in 1966
Reprinted 1969
by S.P.C.K.
Holy Trinity Church
Marylebone Road
London N.W.1

Made and printed in Great Britain by
William Clowes and Sons, Limited
London and Beccles

SBN 281 00871 X

Contents

Acknowledgements

Thanks are due to the following for permission to quote from copyright sources:

George Allen & Unwin Ltd: *Facing Life and Death*, edited by H. Guntrip.

American Journal of Nursing (November 1964): "The Death of a Young Man", by Mary C. S. Googe.

American Journal of Psychotherapy (Vol. XI, No. 3, July 1957): "Psychotherapy and the Dying", by Hattie Rosenthal.

The Reverend John Barton: "The Nurse's Dilemma", a personal communication.

The Right Reverend the Bishop of Derby: an extract from his address to the Derby Diocesan Conference in 1962.

Burns & Oates Ltd and Hawthorn Books, Inc., New York: *The Last Rites*, by J. C. Didier.

Cassell & Co. Ltd: *The Elephant Man and Other Reminiscences*, by Sir Frederick Treves.

William Collins Sons & Co. Ltd and Harper & Row, Inc.: *Le Milieu Divin*, by Teilhard de Chardin.

Community of the Resurrection: a prayer from *My Day with Jesus*.

Cresset Press: *Death, Grief and Mourning in Contemporary Britain*, by Geoffrey Gorer.

College of General Practitioners, *Current Medical Abstract for Practitioners* (Vol. 3, No. 2): "Care of the Dying", by Cicely Saunders.

Epworth Press: an extract from the report *Christianity and Nursing to-day*.

Faith Press Ltd: litanies and prayers from *Handmaids of the Sick*.

Guild of St Raphael Quarterly (May 1961): "The Dying Patient", by Paul C. Gibson; (February 1964): "Should the Doctor Tell?"

Hodder & Stoughton Ltd: *Margaret*, by J. D. Ross; *The Chavasse Twins*, by Selwyn Gummer; *Doors of Eternity*, by Sybil Harton.

Hodder & Stoughton Ltd and Beacon Press, Inc., Boston, Mass.: *Man's Search for Meaning*, by Viktor Frankl.

International Universities Press, Inc., New York: *The Psychiatrist and the Dying Patient*, by K. R. Eissler.

Journal of American Medical Association: "Management of the Patient with Terminal Illness", by P. S. Rhoads.

Journal of Church of England's Hospital Chaplains' Fellowship (February 1965).

Journal of Pastoral Care (Vol. XVII, No. 2, Summer 1964) "The Treatment of the Dying", by T. P. Hackett and A. D. Weisman, reprinted with permission of the authors and publisher, Grune & Stratton, Inc., from Vol. II of *Current Psychiatric Therapies*, edited by Dr Jules H. Masserman; (Winter 1960): "A Study of Terminal Cancer Patients", by Robert Reeves.

Lancet, 1963, i, 1: an extract from "Reflections on Ageing and Death".

Longmans, Green & Co. Ltd: *Immortality*, by E. E. Holmes.

The Mercier Press Ltd, Cork and Divine Word Publications, Techny, Illinois: *New Problems in Medical Ethics*, by Dom Peter Flood.

A. R. Mowbray & Co. Ltd: a prayer from *The People's Missal*, by E. A. L. Clarke.

The Practitioner: "Signs and Symptoms of Impending Death", by Lord Horder.

Routledge & Kegan Paul Ltd: *Human Relations and Hospital Care*, by Ann Cartwright.

Staples Press Ltd: *Nervousness, Indigestion and Pain*, by W. C. Alvarez.

Charles C. Thomas, Inc., Illinois: *Care of the Aged, the Dying and the Dead*, by A. Worcester.

The Times (21 February 1914): letter from Professor Cook Wilson; (23 February 1914): letter from "Septuagenarian"; (24 February 1914): letter from H. Cameron Gillies M.D.; (25 February 1914): letter from "F.R.C.S."

Preface

Addressing the Manchester Medical Society in 1956, Sir Robert Platt, Professor of Medicine, told his audience that he thought "a wise man . . . should meditate now and then upon death, if only to face it courageously should it announce its coming in advance. . . . I find death a fascinating subject," he continued, "and perhaps at some future time I may be permitted to address you on that theme. If so, I shall, of course, be under the handicap of not being able to speak from personal experience!"

Exactly the same difficulty faces anyone who attempts to write about the subject of dying, for it is one thing to express one's thoughts objectively whilst in health but quite another thing to "face it courageously" when nearing death. The writer can only rely on the thoughts and reflections of those who have been on the very threshold of death themselves, and on personal experience as a hospital chaplain whose privilege it is to minister with others at the bedside of the dying.

The ministry to the dying cannot be viewed in isolation, for the act of dying must not be separated from the act of living. It is but a continuation of the whole process of life. Jeremy Taylor saw how essential "Holy Living" was as a necessary preparation for "Holy Dying". Yet preparing people for death is no light task, and few there be who find it other than onerous and difficult. Not least among its problems is the taboo that enshrouds all thought of death in gloom and despair, and such attempts to screen death from our minds, far from resolving the problems involved, serve only to compound the difficulties in facing it. In the recent past there has been a distinct lack of teaching on death, and

the use of prayers for the dying has been by no means
common. Until this is in some way remedied our whole
ministry will remain thwarted and the doctrine of the "Communion of Saints" a neglected dogma of our Creed.

I have undertaken, in Chapter 1, an historical survey of
the "art of dying" literature of the Middle Ages which
formed a literary genre of its own. The survey is by no means
comprehensive but serves as a salutary reminder of the serious
thought given to the subject of death by our forefathers.
Chapter 2 attempts to deal with some of the more common
fears of dying, and how they can best be met. The very real
problem of "to tell or not to tell" is discussed in Chapter 3
with no clear-cut answers to this question, for generaliza-
tions have no place in such a debate. The three essential
qualities for the doctor outlined by Sir William Jenner will
also apply to the priest under such circumstances: "He must
be honest, he must be dogmatic, he must be kind." The
final chapter outlines the rôles of the doctor, the nurse, the
family, the social worker, and the priest in their care of the
dying. In so doing the writer is aware that such duties cannot be precisely defined for there are no set formulas or
"techniques". There can be no rule-of-thumb, for "although
we have travelled this road with our patients, we have not
completed the journey ourselves, and we cannot put ourselves precisely in the position of the patient who is going
the whole way."

The Reverend A. H. F. Purcell Fox, Assistant Chaplain
of the Guild of St Raphael, very kindly read through
Chapter 4, as did Miss Margaret E. Atkin, Senior Medical
Social Worker at the Hospital for Sick Children, Great
Ormond Street. I am grateful for their most helpful suggestions and constructive criticisms. I much appreciate the
permission given by the Reverend John Barton, Chaplain
of Stanley Royd and Pinderfields Hospital, Wakefield, for
the use of *The Nurse's Dilemma*, which forms an appendix
to Chapter 4. For some little time it has been my privilege
to hold discussion groups with the senior nurses of St

George's Hospital Teaching Group during their periods of block-study, in matters relating to the care of the dying. I have much benefited from these consultations, and should like to express my thanks to the nurses in general, and to Miss O. Walden Jones, Principal Tutor, in particular, for making such an arrangement possible in the School of Nursing timetable. My father, the Reverend A. J. Autton, Miss Doris Allan, of Church House, Westminster, and Mrs M. Edwards all shared the rather laborious task of typing the manuscript and I wish to thank them for giving so readily of their time. Miss Doris Allan also very kindly read through the proofs. The Librarians of the St George's Hospital Medical School, School of Nursing, and the Royal College of Nursing, Henrietta Place, W.1, took great trouble and care in supplying the author with copies of relevant books and journals when required. I am also grateful to my publishers, the S.P.C.K., for their co-operation and encouragement, and for permission to quote material from an earlier publication which prompted this larger work—*Death and Bereavement*, a Christian Knowledge Booklet, 1965.

In conclusion I must align myself to the wise words of C. S. Lewis: "For the higher task of teaching fortitude and patience, I was never fool enough to consider myself qualified, nor have I anything to offer my readers except my conviction that when pain is to be borne, a little courage helps more than much knowledge, a little human sympathy much more than courage and the least tincture of the love of God more than all" (*The Problem of Pain*). May the following pages encourage more discussions and further study among all who minister to the dying, for when our mutual concern is centred not so much on the patient because he is dying but on the *person*, then together we may discover "the potential that may become actual at the moment of illumination when the person is aware of himself and is able to say 'I am' before saying 'I am not'."

St George's Hospital, London, S.W.1. **NORMAN AUTTON**
July 1965

PART ONE

The Care of the Dying

"Be ye always ready." Our blessed Saviour does not tell us to begin to prepare ourselves when death has arrived, but to prepare ourselves beforehand; because the time of death will be a time of confusion, when it will be morally impossible to prepare ourselves in a proper manner to appear for judgement, and to obtain a favourable sentence. "It is a just punishment", says St Augustine, "upon him, who having it in his power to do good, will not do it, not to be able to do it afterwards when he desires to do it."

No, my God, I will not wait until that time to begin a change of life. Make known to me what I must now do to please Thee, for I desire to do without reserve whatever Thou requirest of me.   ST ALPHONSUS DE LIGUORI

"So death will come to fetch you?" No, not death, but God Himself. Death is not the horrible spectre we see represented in pictures. The Catechism teaches that death is the separation of the soul from the body; that is all. I am not afraid of a separation which will unite me for ever with God."   ST THÉRÈSE OF LISIEUX

The Door of Death is made of Gold,
That Mortal Eyes cannot behold;
But, when the Mortal Eyes are clos'd,
And cold and pale the Limbs repos'd,
The Soul awakes; and, wond'ring, sees
In her mild Hand the golden Keys;
The Grave is Heaven's golden Gate,
And rich and poor around it wait;
O Shepherdess of England's Fold,
Behold this Gate of Pearl and Gold!

WILLIAM BLAKE

Oh, my Lord and Saviour, support me in that hour in the strong arms of Thy Sacraments, and by the fresh fragrance of Thy consolations. Let the absolving words be said over me, and the holy oil sign and seal me, and Thy own Body be my food, and Thy blood my sprinkling; and let my sweet Mother, Mary, breathe on me, and my Angel whisper peace to me, and my glorious Saints...smile upon me: that in them all, and through them all, I may receive the gift of perseverance, and die, as I desire to live, in Thy faith, in Thy Church, in Thy service, and in Thy love. Amen.

JOHN HENRY NEWMAN

1

The Art of Dying
Ars Moriendi

Then He Himself for death disposed,
Of dying well the art disclosed....
"Since Jesus you the art of dying taught!"
Said Conscience, "Keep death always in your thoughts".
       BISHOP KEN (*Preparatives for Death*).

Dying is an art, like everything else.
       SYLVIA PLATH (*Lady Lazarus*)

The hardest thing of all—to die *rightly*.
—an exam nobody is spared—and how many pass it?
       DAG HAMMARSKJÖLD (*Markings*)

"It is a great art to die well, and to be learnt by men in health." So wrote Jeremy Taylor in the dedicatory section of his *Holy Living and Holy Dying*. To those of his generation to make a good death was seen to be an art—to be acquired by a lifetime of preparation. It was truly "the science of all sciences".

In the Middle Ages the thought of death was constantly in the minds of those who had witnessed half the population of Europe perishing as a result of the Black Death of 1349. Pestilence, hunger, and disease were ever-present dangers, and the subject of death gained pictorial expression in the paintings of Holbein and other artists of that era. Death became personified in the Miracle Plays and the "Dance of Death". Liddon,[1] preaching one of his Advent sermons in St Paul's Cathedral, reminds his congregation that "there was a famous representation of it (i.e. Dance of Death) in the cloister attached to the old St Paul's, and it was engraved in the margin of Queen Elizabeth's Prayer-Book; Death, as a skeleton with a scythe, was represented as approaching men in every rank of society, in every order of Church and State: the monarch, the prelate, the man of learning, the man of business, the squire, the physician, the lawyer, the minstrel, the soldier, the hermit. Each estate was represented so that all beholders might be impressed with the fact that none would escape the visit of death."

The subject of death became a favourite theme, and a solemn preparation for it soon became evident. Specific literature on "the art of dying" began to circulate and became essential reading. One of the earliest works of this nature comes from the pen of Blessed Henry Suso, d. 1365, the German Dominican spiritual writer, called the *Horologium Sapientiae* ("Eternal Wisdom"). "Every day", writes Suso, "I will be on the watch for death, and will look about me that he take me not by surprise. I will learn how to die; I will turn my thoughts to yonder world. Lord, I see that there is no remaining here; Lord, in sooth, I will not save up my sorrow and repentance till death." It was probably from Suso that Jean Charlier de Gerson (1363–1429) gained help in the compilation of his *Opusculum tripartitum* ("Threefold Treatise"), a small portion of which is devoted to the art of dying. In this section, "De arte moriendi", he stresses the help that friends can be during the last hours of life. The dying person is to be admonished to pay attention to the state of his soul, and he outlines six questions (with answers), with the promise to lead a better life if the dying person recovers. He is to take his Holy Communion, and prayers should be recited over him. A crucifix or the image of a saint should be held over the dying, and Gerson emphasizes the danger of raising false hopes in the patient. Invocations are made to God, the Virgin Mary, his guardian angel, and the saints. The work was considered so important that it is said the French clergy of that day were instructed by their bishops to read a section of it to their congregations every Sunday.

With the introduction by Caxton of the printing-press, these booklets had a wider circulation and a deeper appeal. Woodcuts also became a popular addition to the literature.[2] Death was depicted as a sort of battlefield with Satan and his evil spirits fighting to gain possession of the dying soul. Such features could now be given ample and free pictorial expression.

In 1490–1 Caxton translated and printed the *Arte and Crafte to Knowe Well to Dye*, or the *Ars Moriendi*. The author of this popular medieval work is unknown, but it is evident that he was influenced much by Gerson's earlier writing. The *Ars Moriendi* is divided into six sections. The first collects together various texts from the Fathers on the subject of death, and comprises a "commendacyon of dethe and cunnynge to die wel". Moriens, who is the central figure in the book, is persuaded to offer up his soul "gladlye and wilfully". The next section is devoted to the "temptacions of men that dyene"—unbelief, despair, impatience, vainglory, and attachment to relations and earthly possessions—and the method of resisting these when the devil challenges (cf. The Book of Job). Various questions are formulated and suitable prayers are compiled

for to induce him that is sick and laboureth in his dying to very trust and confidence that he should principally have to God at that time, the disposition of Christ on the cross should greatly draw him. Of the which St Bernard saith thus: What man is he that should not be ravished and drawn to hope, and have full confidence in God, and he take heed diligently of the disposition of Christ's body on the cross. Take heed and see: His Head is inclined to salve thee; His mouth to kiss thee; His arms spread to be-clip [embrace] thee; his hands thrilled [pleased] to give Thee; His Side opened to love thee; His body along strait to give all Himself to thee. Therefore no man should despair of forgiveness, but fully have hope and confidence in God; for the virtue of hope is greatly commendable, and of great merit before God. As the Apostle saith and exhorteth us, "Nolite amittere confidentiam vestram quae magnam habet remunerationem" (Hebrews 10.35). Lose not your hope and confidence in God, the which hath great reward of God.

There follows two sections of interrogations[3] which will ensure salvation if answered in the right and proper manner, Part IV contains an "instruccion with certeyne obsecracions to hem that schullen dye". Moriens is again helped to think of Christ on his Cross:

Christ did five things on the cross [says the writer]...First he prayed on the cross. So a sick man, that is in point of death, he should pray, namely in his heart, if he may not with his mouth....The second was he cried. So should every man in his dying cry strongly with his heart, not with the voice.... The crying of the heart to God is nought else but the great desiring of man to have forgiveness of his sins, and to have everlasting life. The third was he wept. With his bodily eyes and with tears of the heart, in token that so should every man in his dying weep with tears of his heart, that is to say, verily repenting all his misdeeds. The fourth he commendeth his soul to God. So every man in his end, saying thus in heart and mouth: "Lord God, into Thine hands I commend my spirit; for truly Thou boughtest me dear". The fifth was he gave up wilfully his spirit. So every man in his death; that is to say, he should die wilfully, conforming fully therein his own will to God's Will, as he is bound.

Short prayers are appended for Moriens to recite to the Trinity, God the Father, God the Son, the Blessed Virgin, and the angels.

The fifth is mainly addressed to Moriens' friends. The influence of Gerson's earlier "De arte moriendi" is most strong here, and, along with both Suso and Gerson, the writer warns against deceiving the dying with false reassurances.

Every sick man, and every other man that is in peril, should be diligently induced and exhorted that he maketh himself, before all other things, peace with God: receiving spiritual medicines, that is to say the sacraments of Holy Church;

ordaining and making his testament, and lawfully disposing for his household, and other needs, if he hath any to dispose for. And there should not be given first to no man too much hope of bodily heal. But the contrary thereof is now often done of many men, into great peril of souls; and namely of them that actually and openly be drawing and in point hastily to die, for none of them will hear nothing of death. . . . Also present to the sick the image of the crucifix, the which should evermore be about sick men.

The sixth and final part contains prayers to be said by those about the bedside of the dying.

In 1881 W. Harry Rylands edited *Ars Moriendi* complete with eleven woodcuts and George Bullen's explanation of each. Although they are of a rather grotesque nature, it is worth describing each in order, for they teach us much about the imagery of the day.

1. *Temptation against faith.* The sick and thin figure of Moriens is seen in bed, with one devil whispering in his ear, and with a scroll on which is written "Infernus factus est". A second devil in the front of the woodcut points to a heathen king and queen worshipping an idol. On his scroll he has written, "Fac sicut pagani". A third devil is seen pointing to a man who appears to be cutting his own throat. He has "Interficias te ipsum" depicted on his scroll. The work of the fourth devil seems to be to screen from Moriens the vision of God the Father, our Lord, and the Virgin Mary.

2. *Inspiration to faith.* One angel is seen holding a scroll— "Sis firmus in fide". The dying man's good angel comes to his rescue, as three devils say, "Fugiamus, victi sumus", "Frustra laboravimus". Moriens appears a little more cheerful and bright, for in the background are God the Father, our Lord, the Virgin Mary, and Moses, offering consolation.

3. *Temptation to despair.* All whom Moriens has wronged appear, together with six hideous devils, who utter such

accusations as, "Perjurus est", "Fornicatus est", "Occidisti", "Avare vixisti". In the background one devil says, "Ecce peccata tua", with a scroll of the sins of Moriens before him.

4. *Inspiration against despair.* Here are depicted the saints who have experienced the mercy and forgiveness of God. We see St Mary Magdalene with her precious ointment of spikenard; Dismas, the penitent thief; St Peter with the cock symbolizing his denial, and the keys to the Church, the Kingdom; and St Paul being thrown from his horse on the Damascus road. Alongside, an angel consoles Moriens with the words, "Nequaquam desperes". Seeking refuge under the bed is a devil who cries, "Victoria michi nulla".

5. *Temptation to impatience.* Moriens must have succumbed well and truly to the taunts of the devil who cries in triumph, "Quam bene decepi eum", for he has knocked over the bedside stand, with bowl, spoon, and glass, and is in the process of also kicking his doctor who flees in alarm. Moriens' wife consoles her husband with the words, "Ecce quantum penam patitur".

6. *Inspiration to patience.* We now see Moriens inspired by those who have suffered most: St Stephen in monk's habit, St Katherine with her wheel, St Lawrence with the gridiron, St Barbara with her tower, and also our Lord with his crown of thorns and scourges. A devil disappearing under the bed cries, "Sum captivatus".

7. *Temptation to vainglory.* Five horrible devils tempt Moriens to pride in having been successful against his first three temptations. He is being offered three crowns, and his mind is being filled with vainglorious thoughts.

8. *Inspiration against vainglory.* Here are seen three angels, with one pointing to the mouth of Hell and stating, "Superbos punio". Above are the Trinity, and the Virgin Mary, and on the left stands St Anthony with bell and crozier, symbolizing true humility.

9. *Temptation to avarice.* Pointing to the family and friends of Moriens, a devil cries, "Provideas amicis". Another points to his possessions with the words, "Intendo thesauro".

10. *Inspiration against avarice.* Close to Moriens is depicted the figure of our Lord on the Cross, with Mary his Mother sorrowing at his side. The first angel says, "Non sis avarus"; the other, "Ne intendas amicis".

11. *The death of Moriens.* Here Moriens is shown for the only time on the left of the woodcut. His soul, in the form of a young child, is passing from his body towards one of the group of four angels behind his bed. On the right hand six devils are hastily retreating—"Confusi sumus", "Heu insania", "Animam amisimus", "Furore consumor", "Spes nobis nulla". On the left hand a monk is seen holding a candle in Moriens' hand, and between the two groups of saints, the Virgin Mary, and St Peter, and St John, and St Mary Magdalene, there stands a crucifix.[4]

During the same period there appeared one of the most popular post-Reformation works on the art of dying. This was Thomas Becon's *Sicke Mannes Salve*, in which "the faithfull Christians may learne both how to behaue themselues paciently and thankefully in the tyme of sickenes, and also vertuously to dispose their temporall goods, and finally to prepare themselues gladly and godly to dye". Written by the Puritan leader, *circa* 1560, it is in many ways one of the most remarkable books of this type of literature. It describes a most lengthy (and therefore impracticable) conversation at the deathbed of Epaphroditus with his friends Philemon, Eusebius, Theophile, and Christopher. Great stress is laid on the importance of making a will, and instruction for the funeral and mourning procedures occupy a large portion of the work.

Eusebius: Neighbour Epaphroditus, seeing that God hath richly blessed you with the goods of this world, it were very expedient to remember the poor scholars of the universities of

Cambridge and Oxford. For if they be not maintained, all learning and virtue will decay....

Epaphroditus: I pray you, neighbour Philemon, set in two hundred pounds of money, one hundred to be given unto the University of Cambridge, the other unto Oxford.

Becon is extremely prejudiced against all Roman Catholic practices: "These purgatory-rakers shall neither rake nor scrape for me with their masses and diriges, when I am departed; for I trust no such works; neither do I any thing regard the prayers of such as have 'the belly for their god'."

Also to be contained in his will is a sum of money for the preaching of sermons: "I give for the preaching of fourscore sermons at other times, when it shall be thought most convenient, twenty pounds." He then adds, rather significantly, that "the greatest part of our beneficed men (God help us!) are blind guides, and dumb dogs, not once able to bark". Directions for the funeral are discussed, and Theophilus asks,

Sir, what solemnity will you have at your burial?

Epap.: What mean you?

Theo: Solemn singing, devout ringing, holy censing, priests pattering, candles lightening, torches brenning, communion saying, and such like.

Epap: No kind of superstitious custom do I allow ... as for your holy censing, priests pattering, candles lighting, torches brenning, away with them as things superficial and unprofitable.

The dying man is then reminded that "the custom in times past was that there should be month minds and year minds kept for the dead". Again Epaphroditus protests that he will "have nothing to do with papists nor with their doctrine. God bless them from me." His instructions to his wife contain the following exhortation: "To forbid the marriage after my departure, according to the property of some husbands, I will not.... Follow not the manners of certain old doting widows, which, for bodily lust, in their crooked age couple themselves to younkers which might well have been their children ... choose thee therefore such a husband that loveth thee ... as is equal to thee in condition, state and age."

After this most animated and protracted dialogue, Epaphroditus makes "a godly end", commending his soul at the last to Almighty God.[5]

In 1595 we have another Puritan, William Perkins, making a contribution to "the art of dying" literature with the publication of his *Salue for a Sicke Man*. The interrogation of the dying (see Part III of the *Ars Moriendi*) comes in for some strong criticism, for Perkins has

> occasion to mention a notorious fault, that is very common in this age, even among such as have long lived in the bosome of the Church; and that is, Men nowadays are so far from renewing their faith and repentance, that when they lie sicke and are drawing toward death, they must be catechized in the doctrine of faith and repentance, as if they had but been of late received into the church. Whosoever will, but as occasion is offered, visit the sick, shall find this to be true... what a shame is this that when a man hath spent his life and dayes in the church ... he should at the very end of all and not before, begin to inquire what faith and what repentance is, and how his soul might be saved. This one sinne argues the great security of this age and the great contempt of God and his Church.

The necessity of giving spiritual help precedence over bodily help (a practice prevalent in the Middle Ages) is stressed, for the "minister is only called in at too late an hour when a man is halfe dead ... drawing on and gasping for breath, as though ministers of the gospel in these daies were able to work miracles".

Perkins also wrote *The Whole Treatise of Cases of Conscience*, which outlines how the dying are to be prepared. In Book I, Chapter 9, Sect. 3, he asks, "How any servant of God may be able to endure with comfort the pangs of death?" For such endurance two things are required: a preparation to death, and helps in the time of death. Concerning preparation, there are three duties to be performed. The first and most principal is commended unto us in the book of Psalms where David praises God, Lord make me to know mine end, and the measure of my days (39.5). And Moses in like manner, Lord teach me to number my days, that I may apply my heart unto wisdom (90.12). In which places is remembered a notable duty of preparation, to wit, that a man should resolve himself of death continually and beforehand number his days. This is done, by esteeming of every day, as the day of his death, and accordingly doing always that which he would do, if he were now to give up the ghost.

Secondly, in way of preparation, we must endeavour to disarm and weaken death, who is as an armed man, that hath his weapons, whereby he seeks to destroy us. And in this case we must deal with death, as the Philistines dealt with Samson ... they laboured to know in what part of his body his strength did lie ... we shall find that his [i.e. death's] weapons are our manifold sins and corruptions both of heart and life. For as St Paul saith, The sting of death is sin (1 Cor. 15.56). Therefore that we may spoil him of this his furniture we must exercise ourselves in the practice of two duties. First, use all means for the cutting off of the lock of our sins ... and these means are the duties of humiliation, invocation and true repentance. We must therefore humble ourselves before God, be instant in prayer for the pardon of our sins past and present. ... Thirdly, in way of preparation, our duty is, even beforehand to endeavour to have some true taste of life everlasting and the joys of heaven ... it will further cause us to say with Simeon, Lord now lettest thou thy servant depart in peace, and with the Apostle, I desire to be dissolved and be with Christ.

In true medieval tradition we also have Sir Thomas More's *Four Last Things* (*circa* 1522). According to Chambers, More "all his life had been studying nothing but dying and being dead",[6] and his *Four Last Things* is an unfinished treatise "upon these words of Holy Scripture— 'remember the last things, and thou shalt never sin' (Ecclus.

7), made about the year of our Lord 1522, by Sir Thomas
More then Knight, and one of the Privy Council of King
Henry VIII, and also Under-Treasurer of England".
Elaborating this text, More tells his readers that

> the physician sendeth his bill to the apothecary, and therein
> writeth sometimes a costly receipt of many strange herbs and
> roots, fetched out of far countries, long-lain drugs, all the
> strength worn out, and none such to be got. But this physician
> sendeth his bill to thyself, no strange thing therein, nothing
> costly to buy, nothing far to fetch, but to be gathered all times
> of the year in the garden of thine own soul. Let me hear, then,
> what wholesome receipt this is, "Remember", saith this bill,
> "thy last things, and thou shalt never sin in this world". Here
> is first a short medicine containing only four herbs, common
> and well known, that is to wit, death, doom, pain and joy.
> This short medicine is of a marvellous force, able to keep us
> all our life from sin.... This medicine serveth every man.
> The physician doth but guess and conjecture that his receipt
> shall do good; but this medicine is undoubtedly sure.

More also makes mention of the Dance of Death under a
section called "The Remembrance of Death": "If we not
only hear this word 'death' but also let sink into our hearts
the very fantasy and deep imagination thereof, we shall per-
ceive thereby that we were never so greatly moved by the
beholding of the Dance of Death pictured in Paul's, as we
shall feel ourselves stirred and altered by the feeling of that
imagination in our hearts."[7]

In the second half of the sixteenth century appeared
Miles Coverdale's *Treatise on Death*. In the first section of
the book (comprising forty brief chapters) there is mention of both prayer and sacrament, but Coverdale takes
strong objection to the private celebration of Holy Communion for use with the dying. "The sacrament of the body
and blood of Christ must be exercised and practised only in
the coming together of the whole congregation and
church, according to the example of the apostles. Therefore
let the sick satisfy himself with the general breaking of

bread, whereof he was partaker with the whole congregation."[8]

We now note the rather interesting development of more and more recognition of the physician and his medicine in cases of sickness, for Coverdale can write that "when one is taken with a disease, to be let blood, to sweat, to follow the physician's instruction; such things are in wise to be reprehended, so that, whether it turn to death or life, the heart only and hope hang on God". He can also tell his readers that "physic is permitted of God, as in the time of pestilence with fires and perfumes to make the air more wholesome from poison, and to receive somewhat into the body, for the consuming of evil humors, and to hinder the infection".[9]

A book of this period that ran into over thirty editions was *The Practice of Pietie*, the work of the Right Reverend Lewis Bayly, Lord Bishop of Bangor. Quotations from the Scriptures abound and much of the earlier traditions is incorporated, but what is new in Bayly's writing is his guidance for the comfort of visitors. He instructs them to "have a specialle care not to stand dumb, and staring in the sick persons face to disquiet him, nor to speak idly, and to ask unprofitable questions.... If they see therefore that the sicke partie is like to die let them not dissemble: but lovingly and discreetly admonish him of his weaknesse, and to prepare for eternall life. One houre well spent, when a mans life is almost outspent, may gaine a man the assurance of eternall life: sooth him not with the vaine hope of this life, lest thou betray this soule to eternall death."

Here again we have stress laid on the duty of making a will, and Bayly warns parents to make provision in good time for their children. Otherwise "they thanke deathe and not thee for the portion that thou leavest them". Let them do it in their lifetime, for "most of other mens Executors prove almost Executioners".

Mention must be made, too, of the *Manual of Directions for the Sick* (1626), by Bishop Lancelot Andrewes, although this may not be in the true line of "the art of dying" book-lets. Andrewes used this manual himself during his incumbency at St Giles, Cripplegate. It contains appropriate and selective passages of Scripture for the comfort of the sick person, morning and evening prayers, and devotions for Holy Communion. Different methods of pastoral approach are prescribed for different classes of people, and are varied according to age, character, and education. Andrewes is known to have possessed a copy of the *Arte and Crafte to knowe Well to Dye*, and probably his own work is influenced by his use of it.

During Lent, 1630, John Donne delivered his famous sermon, *Death's Duell, or, A Consolation to the Soule, against the dying life, and living death of the body*. It was "delivered in a sermon at White-Hall, before the Kings Majesty, in the beginning of Lent (Feb. 25), 1630. Being his last Sermon and called by his Majesties household The Doctors Owne Funerall Sermon." In the preface to the first edition (1632), we are told by Richard Redmer, the publisher, that this sermon "was preached not many dayes before his death; as if, having done this, there remained nothing for him to doe, but to die: and the subject is, of Death". Izaak Walton describes the scene for us as the Dean is about to deliver the sermon:[10]

> When to the amazement of some of the beholders, he appeared in the pulpit, many of them thought he presented himself not to preach mortification by a living voice, but mortality by a decayed body, and a dying face. And doubtless many did secretly ask that question in Ezekiel—"Do these bones live?", or, can that soul organise that tongue to speak so long time as the sand in that glass will move towards its centre, and measure out an hour of this dying man's unspent life? Doubtless it cannot!

After a picture of Donne had been drawn by "a choice painter", and an urn made for his burial, he

> caused it to be set by his bedside, where it continued and became his hourly object till his death, and was then given to his

dearest friend and executor, Dr Henry King, the chief Residentiary of St Paul's, who caused him to be thus carved in one entire piece of white marble, as it now stands in that church.[11]

During the severe illness he was to suffer in the winter of 1623, he published his *Devotions upon Emergent Occasions*, and here, too, the shadow of death was for ever uppermost in his thoughts. It is in No. XVII of the *Devotions*, headed "Now, this Bell tolling softly for another, saies to me, Thou must die", that we have some of his most memorable words.

Perchance hee for whom this Bell tolls, may be so ill, as that he knowes not that it tolls for him, and perchance I may think my selfe so much better than I am, so that they who are about mee, and see my state, may have caused it to toll for mee, and I know not that. The Church is Catholike, universall, so are all her actions. All that she does, belongs to all. When she baptizes a child, that action concerns mee, for that child is thereby connected to that Head which is my Head too, and engraffed into that body, whereof I am a member. And when she buries a Man, that action concernes me: All mankinde is of one Author, and is one volume; when one Man dies, one chapter is not torne out of the booke, but translated into a better language; and every Chapter must be so translated: God emploies several translators; some peeces are translated by age, some by sicknesse, some by warre, some by justice; but Gods hand is in every translation; and his hand shall binde up all our scattered leaves againe, for that Librarie where every booke shall lie open to one another; As therefore the Bell that rings to a Sermon, calls not upon the Preacher onely, but upon the congregation to come; so this Bell calls us all. ... No man is an Iland, intire of it selfe; every man is a peece of the Continent, a part of the maine; if a Clod bee washed away by the Sea, Europe is the lesse, as well as if a Promontorie were, as well as if a Mannor of thy friends or of thine owne were; any mans deathe diminishes me, because I am involved in Mankinde; And therefore never send to know for whom the bell tolls; It tolls for thee.[12]

Five years after Donne's *Death's Duell*, there appeared the famous *Religio Medici* of Sir Thomas Browne, the meditative writer and physician. Donne before him had made much of the comparison of death with sleep. "Death is but a sleepe. Many have wondered at that note of Saint Chrysostom's, That till Christ's time death was called death, plainly, literally death, but after Christ, death was called but sleepe; for indeede, in the old-Testament before Christ, I thinke there is no one metaphor so often used, as Sleepe for Death, and that the Dead are said to Sleepe."[13] Again in his *Devotions*, Donne can say that "Every nights bed is a Type of the grave".[14] Browne elaborates the same theme.

Sleep is that death by which we may be literally said to die daily; a death which Adam died before his mortality; a death whereby we live a middle and moderating point between life and death; in fine, so like death, I dare not trust it without my prayers and an half adieu unto the World, and take my farewell in a Colloquy with God....

> Sleep is a death: O make me try,
> By sleeping, what it is to die:
> And as gently lay my head
> On my grave, as now my bed....

This is the Dormitive I take to bedward: I need no other Laudanum than this to make me sleep; after which I close mine eyes in security, content to take my leave of the Sun, and sleep unto the Resurrection.

Religio Medici is more a private confession of faith than a work devoted to the subject of death, although, as we have noted, mention is made of it. Indeed it was never intended for the public but merely as a "private exercise and satisfaction". Browne has a rather illuminating comment on suicide as well. "This", he writes, "is not indeed to fear death, but yet to be afraid of life." He also adds, "It is a brave act of valor to condemn death but, where life is more terrible than death, it is then the truest valor to dare to live." Perhaps even more famous is his *Hydriotaphia*, or *Urn Burial* (1658). These are a series of sombre speculations on death, immortality, and the vanity of human life. Certain burial urns containing supposedly Roman remains were discovered at the time in Norfolk.

Jeremy Taylor's classic, *Holy Dying*, appeared in 1651, written in beautiful seventeenth-century prose. Taylor prefaces the work thus: "The Rule and Exercises of Holy Dying. In which are described the MEANS and INSTRUMENTS of preparing ourselves and others respectively for a blessed Death; and the Remedies against Evils and Temptations proper to the state of Sickness; Together with Prayers and Acts of Virtue to be used by Sick and Dying persons, or by others standing in their attendance. To which are added Rules for the Visitation of the Sick, and offices proper for that Ministry." Taylor sees the whole course of life as a school for dying well. (The first volume of the book is *Holy Living*, as a necessary and vital preparation.) Unlike some of the earlier literature outlined above, Jeremy Taylor writes with the presence of the priest very much in mind, and in Chapter V, Section 2, condemns those who fear the presence of the priest at the bedside of the sick and dying.

> It is a very great evil both in the matter of prudence and piety, that men fear the priest as they fear the embalmer or the sexton's spade; and love not to converse with him unless they can converse with no man else; and think his office so much to relate to the other world that he is not to be treated with while we hope to live in this; and, indeed, that our religion be taken care of only when we die: and the event is this (of which I have seen some sad experience), that the man is deadly sick, and his reason is useless, and he is laid to sleep, and his life is in the confines of the grave, so that he can do nothing towards the trimming of his lamp; and the curate shall say a few prayers by him, and talk to a dead man, and the man is not in a condition to be helped, but in a condition to need it hugely.

Rather, says Taylor, "let the spiritual man come when the sick man can be conversed withal and instructed, when he can take medicine and amend, when he understands or can be taught to understand the case of his soul, and the rules of his conscience. . . ." As in the former works of this type of literature, the temptations are outlined and appropriate "remedia" prescribed. Angels and devils also do battle in line with the traditions of the age. The final chapter (V) provides a set of rules for the priest's ministry to the dying, and the work concludes fittingly with appropriate prayers.

In the same year as Taylor's *Holy Dying* there was published a somewhat similar work by a Huguenot scholar, Charles Drelincourt, *The Consolations of the Faithful Soul against the Terrors of Death*.[15] It is a longer work than Taylor's classic, but inferior to it. After contending that the heathen philosophers offered no real consolation to the dying, he makes mention of a series of "remedia" to be employed against fears of death. These are then followed by "consolations". At the end of twenty-four lengthy chapters there appear twenty-nine prayers to be used for different types of people (cf. Bishop Launcelot Andrewes).

The *Reformed Pastor* of Richard Baxter was published in 1656 and, like Taylor before him, the author insists that visits to the dying should commence before death approaches. The pastor should "do the office of inferior Angels for the soul before it is departed from the flesh, that it may be ready for the convoy of superior Angels, to transmit it to the prepared glory when it is removed from sin and misery. When a man is almost at his journey's end . . . it is time for us to help him if we can, while there is hope." This is followed by some sound advice which still has present-day application. "Stay not till strength and understanding be gone, and the time so short that you scarce know what to do; but go to them as soon as you hear that they are sick (whether they send for you or not). When the time is short . . . we must therefore be sure to ply the main, and dwell upon those truths which must do the great work, showing them the certainty and glory of the life to come, and the way by which it was purchased for us."

Baxter's earlier work, *Saints Everlasting Rest*, is not quite in the same category, for its primary purpose is not to prepare the reader for a good death, but is written for "those whose portion is heaven, whose hopes are there, and who

3

have forsaken all to enjoy this glory". Writing to his "dearly beloved Friends, the Inhabitants of the Borough and Foreign of Kidderminster" on 15 January 1649/50, he out-lines his reasons for writing the book.

> Being my quarters, far from home, cast into extreme languishing by the sudden loss of about a gallon of blood, after many years of foregoing weaknesses, and having no ac-quaintance about me, nor any books but my Bible, and living in constant expectation of death, I bent my thoughts on my Everlasting Rest; and because my memory through extreme weakness, was imperfect, I took my pen and began to draw up my own funeral sermon, or some helps for my own medita-tion of heaven, to sweeten both the rest of my life and my death.

Believing as Baxter did that impenitent souls would suffer everlasting damnation, he is eager to warn his readers with some searching questions.

> If you die tomorrow, how unready are you? And with what terrors will your souls go out of their bodies? And do you yet loiter for all this? Why, consider with yourselves, God standeth all this while waiting your leisure; His Patience beareth: His Justice forbeareth; His Mercie intreateth you: Christ standeth offering you his blood and merits; you may have Him freely and life with Him; the Spirit is persuading you; Conscience is accusing and urging you; ministers are praying for you, and calling upon you; Satan stands waiting when Justice will cut off your lives, that he may have you. This is your time! Now or never![16]

The well-known historian of the Reformation, Gilbert Burnet (1643–1715), Bishop of Salisbury, compiled a *Dis-course of the Pastoral Care*, in which Chapter VIII is de-voted to "The Functions and Labours of Clergy-men". Commenting on death-bed repentance, Burnet warns that

> unless the Sickness has been of a long continuance, and that the Person's Repentance, his Patience, his Piety has been very extraordinary during the Course of it, he must be sure to give him no positive ground of Hope; but leave him to the

Mercies of God. For there cannot be any greater Treachery to Souls, that is more fatal and more pernicious, than the giving quick and easie hopes, upon so short, so forced, and so imperfect a Repentance.... So the hopes that are given to Death-bed Penitents must be a most effectual means to root out the Sense of Religion of the Minds of all that see it; and therefore though no dying Man is to be driven to Despair, and left to die obstinate in his Sins ... yet after all, the best thing a Dying Man can do, is to Repent; if he recovers that may be the Seed and Beginning of a new Life and a new Nature in him.

At the close of the seventeenth century came John Kettlewell's *Death made Comfortable; or, the Way to Die Well* (1695). Kettlewell, Vicar of the Warwickshire parish of Coleshill for almost forty years, and friend of Bishop Ken, is anxious to show his people "what will render their sick-bed carriage rewardable, and its sorrows tolerable and comfortable. How they are like to be most easy to themselves, and may most profitably chuse or improve the company and employ and receive the services and kind offices of others. What they are to do, that they may die well, and be happy and full of comfort in their death, and after it; and how it is fit for them to part with all men, and take a decent and a Christian leave of this world." In the Preface he points out that death "is a thing, which all men know, and all men fear. And they who study most to keep the thoughts of Death far from them do yet certainly know that it will come. And happy then is he, whose mind is so well prepared and fortified that it can never fright nor hurt him, who has disarmed this King of Terrors (Job 18.14) and made this great enemy of Nature to become a Friend. . . . All this religion will do if we will make a right use of it, for the sting of death is sin, and true repentance takes that out." Mention is made of the "admonisher" at the bedside of the dying, whose duty it is to see that those around do not unnecessarily disturb the dying and so increase his pains. If they are troublesome in this way, they must be turned out. Also

the dying person must be left to make whatever arrange-
ments he wishes about his own funeral.

To an age which largely sees death as an anachronism,
much of the teaching on the "ars moriendi" outlined in
the works of the Middle Ages will appear distressingly
morbid. To a certain degree, of course, this is understandable. Few, if any, would wish to-day to imitate the example
of Donne, who lay in his coffin as a constant reminder of
death. Few, too, would deem it desirable to revive the
imagery of the woodcuts and the macabre Dance of Death,
but at the same time there is much in the teaching of our
forebears that remains valid and undated; much to remind
us afresh of the fact of death and the art of dying.

From Taylor we can still learn to see life as a preparation
for death, and we can remember "the last things" with
More. From Perkins and Baxter we recall the need for the
priest to be sent for in good time, and with Gerson, we recognize the harmfulness of false and deceitful reassurances.
With Bayly we acknowledge the duty of making provision
for those left behind and of declaring our debts. Andrewes
reminds us of the comfort of prayer and sacrament.

A society which prides itself in its self-sufficiency must re-
discover the folly of viewing death as an embarrassment
and an intrusion. A world which is so much devoted to
material gains and technological advances must be prepared
to relearn the "craft of all crafts", and "the science of all
sciences". When thoughts of death become increasingly
suppressed, fears of it become substantiated. It is to such
fears that we now turn our attention.

2

The Fear of Death

It is not a sin to be afraid, but it
is a great felicity to be without fear.

JEREMY TAYLOR (*Holy Dying*)

Fear death?—to feel the fog in my throat,
    The mist in my face,
When the snows begin, and the blasts denote
    I am nearing the place...

ROBERT BROWNING (*Prospice*)

Yea, though I walk through
the valley of the shadow of death,
I will fear no evil for thou art with me.   *Psalm 23*

The lack of present-day teaching about death and preparation for our last hours upon earth does much to increase our
terror of it. The "great adventure" consequently becomes
the "king of terrors". "Sex" has broken its taboo, but
"death" remains neglected and suppressed. Indeed we avoid
the very words, "death", "dying", and speak rather of
"passing away", "falling asleep", or being "called to higher
service."[1] In an age of "battle, murder, and sudden death",[2]
we still attempt to expel all notion of death from our minds,
and seem to "spend all our lives trying to take our minds off
death" (Pascal). When death does occur, it becomes an embarrassment. In *The Death of Ivan Ilych* by Tolstoy, we
read of Ivan's torment of mind when, realizing he is dying,
he notes the attitude of those about him. He senses that
"the awful, terrible act of his dying was ... reduced by those
about him to the level of a casual, unpleasant, and almost

indecorous incident.... He saw that no one felt for him, because no one even wished to grasp his position."[3]

When we take the trouble to think about death, it is more often than not in an abstract manner. In his *Thoughts for the Times on War and Death,*[4] Freud points out that "in the unconscious every one of us is convinced of his own immortality. As to the death of another, the civilized man will carefully avoid speaking of such a possibility in the hearing of the person concerned . . . our habit is to lay stress on the fortuitous causation of the death—accident, disease, infection, advanced age; in this way we betray our endeavour to modify the significance of death from a necessity to an accident." We are apt to amend the words of the Psalmist and cry that although "a thousand shall fall beside me, and ten thousand at my right hand, it shall not come nigh *me!*" Yet strangely enough we seem to find a certain amount of fascination and interest in "detached" death, or in a death which is somehow innocuous and superficial, finding complete relaxation in television films and detective stories in which dozens of people get killed or murdered. The eternal issues of death give way to a concentration upon the circumstances of death.

A fear of death is both normal and natural. Indeed Simcox[5] can say that "the absence of this anxiety from any individual is so abnormal that the rest of us regard it as insanity . . . one who is indifferent to whether he lives or dies, cannot be in his right mind. The existence of the anxiety of death is a mark of sanity." Writing "On the Gospel of St John" (Tractate LX), St Augustine asks, "Ought the mind of the Christian to be troubled even at the prospect of death?", and replies thus.

> Strong-minded, indeed, are those Christians, if such there are, who experience no trouble at all in the prospect of death; but for all that, are they stronger-minded than Christ? Who would have the madness to say so? And what else, then, does His being troubled signify, but that, by voluntarily assuming

the likeness of their weakness, He comforted the weak members in His body, that is in His Church; to the end that, if any of His own are still troubled at the approach of death, they may fix their gaze upon Him, and so be kept from thinking themselves castaways on this account, and being swallowed up in the more grievous death of despair?

The fear to be overcome is that which has no hope or assurance. This fear prompts us to "flee from the reality of our eventual deaths with such purpose and persistence, and employ defences so patently magical and regressive that these would be ludicrously obvious to us if we should employ them to this degree in any other area of human conflict."[6] In this respect, it is not without significance that among the more neglected of the doctrines of our Creed are "The Communion of Saints; The Forgiveness of sins; The Resurrection of the body, And the life everlasting". Our subconscious fears and anxieties of death can lead to a high percentage of nervous breakdowns and admissions to psychiatric hospitals. To understand death we must be prepared to confront it, and become aware of the fact of personal death. Even the pagan world had its "memento mori", for

> Wise in his day that heathen emperor,
> To whom, each morrow, came a slave, and cried—
> "Philip, remember thou must die": no more.[7]

What are some of the commoner fears of death which torment the human mind?

1. THE MYSTERY OF DEATH[8]

Here we are up against the difficulty of describing, or rather imagining, what will actually happen at the moment of death, or immediately afterwards. No one has returned to tell what happens, for the hereafter is "an undiscover'd country from whose bourne no traveller returns", and with Hamlet (Act iii, Sc. 1) we have to confess that this "puzzles the will". Science, with all its advances, "has not succeeded in putting death into its crucibles or test tubes and explaining it; and to-day men stand as awe-stricken and puzzled in the presence of that great mystery as did our ancestors a thousand years ago".[9] In the deathbed scene of Fr Lucero in *Death comes for the Archbishop*, Willa Cather dramatically describes the feelings of those around in their eagerness to solve this mystery of what lies in the great beyond. "Among the watchers there was always the hope that the dying man might reveal something of what he alone could see; that his countenance, if not his lips, would speak, and on his features would fall some light or shadow from beyond ... the dying murmurs of every common man and woman were listened for and treasured by their neighbour and kinsfolk. These sayings, no matter how unimportant, were given oracular significance and pondered by those who must one day go the same road" (p. 167).

The silence of our Lord on the life hereafter is most marked, but we do have his reassurance that in his Father's house there are many mansions, or "resting-places". Words would surely fail to describe the glories of the unknown, as one who himself was once on the brink of death could say: "So I lay, upon the edge of death looking out.... It lay just there—that great Beyond, and I saw it as one sees the earth at sunrise ... yet how, it was difficult to tell, for the things outside this world are outside this world's speech." If more knowledge were to be granted us, and we no longer saw through a glass darkly, we should probably long with St Paul "to depart and be with Christ".[10]

> Dear beautious Death, the jewel of the just,
> Shining nowhere but in the dark;
> What mysteries do lie beyond thy dust,
> Could man outlook that mark.[11]

2. THE LONELINESS AND SEPARATION OF DEATH

Every one of us will have to do our dying alone. "Think what it is to lie on thy deathbed, when all the pleasures of life withdraw themselves, and bid thee eternally adieu. Then thou wilt be left alone, though thou wert lord over millions, nor can any force of armed men defend thee from that mortal stroke."[12] The saying of Pascal, "I shall be alone in death", solemnly reminds us of this. They are words that Liddon described as "the most useful that a man can keep in his memory, or rather, can repeat to himself, in the privacy of his home, and also every morning and evening of his life".[13]

Ivan Ilych (*The Death of Ivan Ilych*), "calling to mind with what regularity he had been going downhill", and with every possibility of hope shattered, experiences "a loneliness in the midst of a populous town and surrounded by numerous acquaintances and relations but that yet could not have been more complete anywhere—either at the bottom of the sea or under the earth. . . ." There is a natural reluctance to leave the ties of human affection behind as well as all that we have held dear. This is dramatically illustrated for us by one of the entries in the diary kept by Captain Scott of the Antarctic. "We are here", he wrote, "face to face with one of the things that makes it hard to die. It is the parting from objects or persons that hold a large place in our affections; for the ties of human love are too exquisitely tender to be harshly torn asunder without provoking acute pain." Death disrupts our union with the world, with our nearest and dearest, and with our own body.

To the Christian, however, death does not result in final absence but in an eternal presence, for "God cannot behold any human death without being recalled to the presence of the death of Christ. A sight such as Calvary is not forgotten: the Father, if we may speak in an anthropomorphical manner which is here justifiable, never ceases to be moved by it. Seeing any man die, God sees again the death of Christ on the Cross."[14] The Communion of Saints teaches us that we shall again be reunited with those whom we have loved on earth, for love and friendship are stronger than death. "This is the faith that sustains me", says Donne, "when I lose by the death of others, or when I suffer by living in misery myselfe. That the dead and we, are now all in one Church, and at the resurrection, shall be all in one Quire."[15]

3. THE CORRUPTION AND DECAY OF DEATH

There is in the mind of man a revulsion against death, for men fear to cease being themselves (cf. Barbellion—"I hate death because I should cease to be I". Also, the comment of a patient—"I am not afraid of death. But I must admit I am very apprehensive about the process of dying with all of its messiness and indignity."[16]) Death seems to have a certain indignity about it. It is a humiliation, an insult, an affront to our very being, and as Tillich points out in his *The Courage to Be*, it is this threat of "non-being" that makes our anxiety of death most basic, "for existentially everybody is aware of the complete loss of self which biological extinction implies" (p. 40). In Donne's *Death's Duell* it is described as "this posthume death, this death after death, nay this death after buriall, this dissolution after dissolution, this death of corruption and putrefaction, of vermiculation and incineration, of dissolution and dispersion in and from the grave". Thomas Browne in his *Religio Medici* (p. 53) confesses that he is "naturally bashful, nor hath conversation, age or travell, beene able to effront, or enharden me, yet I have one part of modesty which I have seldome discovered in another, that is (to speake truly), I am not so much afraid of death, as ashamed thereof. It is the very disgrace and ignominy of our natures, that in a moment can so disfigure us that our nearest friends, wife and children stand afraid and start at us..." Yet Browne can conclude that "marshalling all the horrours, and contemplating the extremities thereof, I finde not any thing therein able to daunt the courage of a man, much less a well resolved Christian!"[17]

Many potential suicides are probably an open rebellion against this dread of the decay of the body through disease and pain. The horror of death "depends not so much on the pain that often accompanies dissolution as upon the mystery of it, and the results to the subject and to the survivors—the cessation of the old familiar relations between them and the decomposition of the body. This horror has given rise to an obstinate disbelief in the necessity of death, and to attempts continually repeated in spite of invariable disastrous experience of failure, to escape it.... The picture thus presented of the desperate refusal of mankind to accept a cardinal condition of experience is one of the most pathetic in the history of the race."[18]

To combat this horror we have words of reassurance from the pen of George Herbert:

> Death, thou wast once an uncouth hideous thing,
>   Nothing but bones,
>   The sad effect of sadder groans:
> Thy mouth was open, but thou couldst not sing.
>
> For we consider'd thee as at some six
>   Or ten years hence,
>   After the loss of life and sense,
> Flesh being turned to dust, and bones to sticks.
>
> But since our Saviour's death did put some blood
>   into thy face;
>   Thou art grown fair and full of grace....

4. UNREPENTED SIN AND JUDGEMENT

"It is appointed unto men once to die, but after this the judgement" (Hebrews 9.27). As we look back over our past lives, most of us will be forced to recall that "we have followed too much the devices and desires of our own hearts", and "have offended against thy holy laws". Many opportunities have been neglected and privileges misused. The account of our stewardship must now be given. It is a sober and fearful thought that "if we dye ill once, we shall never be allowed to dye again, to see if we would dye better the second time".[19]

St Augustine confesses that "nothing has contributed more to wean me away from an idle preoccupation with trivial things than the thought of death and the last account". William Souter, one of the most accomplished of modern Scottish poets, has left for us a day-to-day diary of his thoughts and feelings as he lay dying. In his *The Diaries of a Dying Man*[20] he writes the following entry under 9 July 1942: "To know that one is nearing the end of his life becomes a revelation of how dilatory one has been in the years when death seemed far away. My own days have been but loosely filled with accomplished tasks; in comfort and quiet, the tempo of one's living tends to become more and more easy-moving; the fulfilling of one's busyness more and more liable to be prolonged by the thought—'There is always tomorrow'. So much that I ought to have completed remains fragmentary or wholly unexpressed."

Some words of Bishop Fulton Sheen in *Peace of Soul* (p. 221) remind us of the solemn fact that death "will reveal the *real me* as against the *surface me*. The soul will stand naked before God, seen at last as it truly is . . . each and every one must step forward, alone, out of the ranks. There will be no attorneys to plead our case, no alienists to argue that we were not in our right minds when we did wrong. There will be only one voice: it will be the voice of conscience which will reveal us as we really are."

In the sacramental ministry of the Church the comfort of the sacrament of penance enables us to pass into the presence of God with the divine words of absolution ringing in our ears. The way in which we live will therefore make a difference to the way in which we die.

5. THE AGONY OF DYING

We must first distinguish between a fear of dying and the fear of death. "Death itself does not frighten me; it is the

jump I am afraid of", or as David Gray describes it in his
poem "In the Shadows":

> "I fear not death, but dying"—not the long
> Hereafter, sweetened by immortal love;
> But the quick, terrible last breath—the strong
> Convulsion. Oh, my lord of breath above!
> Grant me a quiet end, in easeful rest—
> A sweet removal, on my mother's breast.

It is the testimony of those who have been nearest to the
dying, or on the verge of death itself, that we leave this
world very much as we enter it. Although the fear of death
might have been strong throughout the lives of many, few
express fear when their death approaches. So often the real
agony is in the anticipation rather than in the realization.

In *The Adventure of Death*,[21] Robert W. Mackenna can
say that his experience "has been that, however much men
and women may, when in the full vigour of health, fear
death, when the hour approaches the fear is almost invari-
ably stilled in gentleness, and they face the end with calm-
ness and a serene mind". H. Sainsbury tells us that "the
sting of death is in the foretaste.... However grim-visaged
he may appear in the approaches, even in the forecourts, in
the Presence Chamber he is wont to unmask and reveal the
face of a friend ... his victory assured and accepted there
follows peace, and for the wounds which he himself in-
flicted, it is his custom to administer an unfailing opiate—
in a drowsiness we take our departure."[22] We also have the
well-known words of Sir John Hunter, the famous surgeon:
"If I had the strength to hold a pen I would write down
how easy and pleasant a thing it is to die." Such an authority
as Sir Frederick Treves[23] describes the last moments of life
as

> more distressing to witness than to endure. What is termed
> the agony of death concerns the watcher by the bedside rather
> than the being who is the subject of pity. A last illness may be
> long, wearisome and painful, but the closing moments of it
> are, as a rule, free from suffering. There may appear to be a

terrible struggle at the end, but of this struggle the subject is unconscious. It is the onlooker who bears the misery of it. . . . Quite commonly the actual instant of death is preceded, for hours or days, by total unconsciousness. In other instances a state of semi-consciousness may exist up to almost the last moment of life. It is a dreamy condition, free from all anxiety, a state of twilight when the familiar landscape of the world is becoming very indistinct. In this penumbra friends are recognized, automatic acts are performed, and remarks are uttered which show or seem to show, both reason and purpose. . . . It is, however, so hazy a mental mood that could the individual return to life again no recollection of the period would, I think, survive . . .[24]

That the "agony" is felt more by those who remain than by those who depart is also borne out by the statements found in an unfinished manuscript written during the last four months of his life by the Reverend Leslie Tizard (one-time Minister of Carr's Lane Church, Birmingham). He had been working out his adjustment to the knowledge of his impending death and describes his thoughts thus: "Once you have accepted the idea of death and have become reconciled to it, there is not, I think, any great difficulty about dying. Indeed there may be a sense of relief in letting go and giving up the struggle. In this drama," he continues, "which reaches the final act every day on innumerable stages, it is not the husband or wife who dies but the one remaining behind who bears the heaviest part."[25]

It would also be the testimony of priests ministering to the dying both at home and in hospital that on the faces of the dying there is frequently a blissful peacefulness and resignation, with few signs of fear or terror.[26] In a long protracted illness or severe suffering so often the patient has looked forward to release, and can re-echo the words of Ecclesiasticus—"O death, acceptable is thy sentence unto the needy and unto him whose strength faileth, that is now in the last age, and is vexed with all things, and to him that despaireth and hath lost patience."

It would, however, be misleading to suggest that every deathbed is calm and peaceful, for with some patients there is much mental pain, which, coupled with their physical suffering, makes them demanding, resentful, and difficult. Writing at the beginning of the century, Osler gives us the results which he kept of "about 500 death beds, studied particularly with reference to the modes of death and the sensations of the dying ... ninety suffered bodily pain, or distress of one sort or another, eleven showed mental apprehension, two positive terror. One expressed spiritual exaltation, one bitter remorse. The great majority gave no sign one way or the other; like their birth, their death was a sleep and a forgetting."[27] Two more recent investigations reveal a somewhat different picture, thanks to the advances made with modern drugs to ease pain and relieve the suffering of the dying. The researches undertaken by Exton-Smith[28] and J. M. Hinton[29] are of extreme help to all who have to do with those in the throes of terminal illness. The former study was undertaken with 220 geriatric patients (80 men and 140 women), and the latter with 102 patients dying in general wards of a Teaching Hospital. Hinton reports that "patients more prone to anxiety were those aware of the possibility of dying, those with tepid religious faith, those under fifty years of age, and those with dependent children". The study of terminal illness in the aged revealed that "for the most part approaching death was accepted with resignation and without fear or misgivings. Some became extremely demanding and difficult." Such reports reveal the need for tact, skill, and patience in those whose privilege it is to minister to the dying.

The situation is admirably summed up for us in the words of another physician, Paul C. Gibson, who points out

that the so-called agony of dying is really the culmination of the agony of living; it occurred before the struggle was over, before the dying had begun. This reminds us that the Agony of Jesus was in Gethsemane, not on the Cross. The approach to death may be horribly painful, but the pain is in the disease, not in the dying; and the ending may be a hideous show, but the show is not visible to the patient, and the horror more apparent than real. The distorted features and convulsive movements are phenomena of release, due to withdrawal of the restraining influence of higher centres over the powerful reflex mechanism below, but this withdrawal only occurs when consciousness is in abeyance. The so-called agony of dying is a myth, wrongly interpreted. . . .[30]

Although personal sanctity is no talisman against the fears of death, for "the unit must share in the sin of the aggregate, and apart from personal and individual sins, our share in corporate sin, the 'sin of the whole world', may affect us with fear and amazement", we know that the real fear of death has been removed for us by our Lord so that we, too, can cry with St Paul, "O Death, where is thy sting?" By means of the Passion, Death, and glorious Resurrection the ugly, gruesome, and unpleasant fact of death has been transformed. We have only to think of what our state would be without death, and if men were endowed with an earthly immortality.

At first they might rejoice and think their last dread enemy destroyed. But what a mistake. In the first place, since none are to be removed from the earth, of course, none must come into it. . . . Thousands of years pass. They have drunk every attainable spring of knowledge dry . . . no terror startles them. No possible experiment remains untried; nor is there any unsounded fortune left. No dim marvels and boundless hopes beckon them into the future. *They have no future.* One everlasting *now* is their all. . . . If it is a Divine boon that men should be, then death is good for us; for it enables us to be men. . . . Give the human race an earthly immortality and you exclude them from every thing greater and diviner than the earth affords. Who could consent to that? . . .[31]

Who indeed! "Wee are happier with death than we should have beene without it" (*Religio Medici*). If we were never doomed to die we should find that "a life of endless possibilities would be nothing but a lazy monotony of boredom and indifference. Unlimited time would mean time exhausted and wasted before it even began. If we knew that man could never die, we should go mad."[32]

If we can practise facing death before it comes—not casting away all thought of it or indeed shrinking from it, but daily learning to approach it courageously, and abandoning ourselves more readily to the will of God—we shall find in our last hours that "the fear of death is shrivelled up like a fragrant moth", and that we can not only in very truth repeat the words of the Psalmist, "Yea, though I walk through the valley of the shadow of death, I will fear no evil: for thou art with me; thy rod and thy staff comfort me", but also address our guardian angel thus:

> Why have I now no fear at meeting Him?
> Along my earthly life, the thought of death
> And judgement was to me most terrible.
> I had aye before me, and I saw
> The Judge severe e'en in the Crucifix.
> Now that the hour is come, my fear is fled,
> And at this balance of my destiny,
> Now close upon me, I can forward look
> With a serenest joy.
>
> ANGEL
> It is because
> Then thou didst fear, that now thou dost not fear,
> Thou hast forestalled the agony, and so
> For thee, the bitterness of death is past.[33]

Appendix

EXTRACTS FROM
CORRESPONDENCE ON THE
PAINLESSNESS OF DEATH
The Times, 1914

The writer's father had heart-failure in his eighty-eighth year after a bout of influenza.

4

I feel it a duty to make them [his experiences] public for the comfort of all those who have to watch what looks like a desperate and conscious fight for breath....

In the last stages there began the rapid laboured breathing which is a familiar feature of such cases. It was most distressing to hear and watch ... the panting was so loud, so quick. ... However, my father, being an exceptionally strong man, survived the dreadful night. In the morning his breathing became much quieter, he recovered consciousness, and became able to speak a little ... he managed to say quite clearly, "Tell the doctor that I have had a very comfortable night". I was astonished and grateful beyond measure to have the best evidence possible in the patient's own testimony.

Professor Cook Wilson, 21 February.

The writer had been on the point of death from double pneumonia.

... so far as I can remember, I felt no physical pain of a struggle for life and breath, and no fear; and the result of my experience is greatly to encourage me in facing when my time comes the inevitable passage into "the valley of the shadow of death".   *"Septuagenarian", 23 February.*

... Where pain is of no use or saving service, as in inevitable death, there is no pain.... The people of my native Highlands ... have a time-old proverb, "there is always peace before death" ("Tha feigh roimh bhas").

H. Cameron Gillies, M.D., 24 February.

... Sir William Savory, F.R.S., in his lectures on *Life and Death* delivered at the Royal Institute 1893, said, "I believe the idea that under every circumstance the moment of death is one of agony to be a widely-spread error. Those who have looked into this subject most closely agree in declaring that usually it is not so." Again, Sir Benjamin Brodie in his Psychological Inquiries wrote, "Really according to my observation, the mere act of dying is seldom in any sense of the word a painful process. I have myself never known but two instances in which, in the act of dying, there were manifest indications of the fear of death."   *"F.R.C.S.", 25 February*

ALL CAUSES OF DEATH

by sex, according to type of institution, etc., in which they occurred, 1957 to 1961, England and Wales.

	1957	1958	1959	1960	1961
PSYCHIATRIC HOSPITALS:					
N.H.S.					
Male	6,297	6,198	6,502	6,458	6,989
Female	8,173	8,790	9,329	9,279	9,933
Other than N.H.S.					
Male	232	207	138	137	145
Female	358	369	278	270	262
OTHER HOSPITALS AND INSTITUTIONS FOR THE CARE OF THE SICK:					
N.H.S.					
Male	115,245	117,541	121,352	123,291	129,975
Female	96,744	101,466	106,478	109,546	117,998
Other than N.H.S.					
Male	4,396	4,586	4,528	4,671	4,627
Female	8,960	9,376	9,528	9,561	9,730
OTHER INSTITUTIONS:					
Male	6,726	6,714	6,587	6,346	6,917
Female	8,202	9,426	9,632	9,589	10,706
AT DECEASED PERSON'S OWN HOME:					
Male	120,259	121,176	116,395	113,327	116,432
Female	115,381	115,624	111,359	107,682	110,584
IN OTHER PRIVATE HOUSES AND OTHER PLACES:					
Male	13,252	14,217	14,376	14,942	15,697
Female	10,645	11,153	11,169	11,169	11,757
TOTAL DEATHS:					
Male	266,407	270,639	269,878	269,172	280,782
Female	248,463	256,204	257,773	257,096	270,970

3

Should the Dying be Told?

"Should the patients be told the truth?"
Pray, which patient and which truth?

BERNARD C. MEYER

1784 (*Aetat* 75) December:
Johnson, with that native fortitude which amidst all his
bodily distress and mental sufferings never forsook him,
asked Dr Brooklesty, as a man in whom he had confidence,
to tell him plainly whether he would recover. "Give me",
said he, "a direct answer." BOSWELL'S *Life of Johnson*.

To everything there is a season, and a time to every purpose
under the heaven: A time to be born and a time to die.

Eccles. 3.1,2.

It is indicative of our lack of teaching about the subject
of death that such a question arises at all, but it is a very
real problem which faces the doctor, chaplain, nurse, and
relative. It is a problem, however, to which there can be no
general answer, for each patient is a unique personality in
a unique situation. It would therefore be as wrong to
state categorically that everyone should be told as to affirm
dogmatically that no one should be told. There can be no
hard and fast rules. Where these are made, they are carried
out not so much to help the patient as to make circumstances easier for everyone else, and avoid the difficulty of
reaching a decision.

Some patients are strong-minded, whilst others are over-
sensitive. There are many who themselves know deep down
that they are going to die, and sense the real situation far

more clearly than we anticipate. A questionnaire[1] sent out to 460 American physicians asking the question "Do you think a person facing death should be told that he is dying?", brought the following results:

If the patient asks	Yes (275) 59·8%	No (76) 16·5%	
Depends on patient	(65) 14·1%	Usually (38) 8·3%	
Unclassified	(6) 1·3%		
If he does not ask	Yes (56) 11·9%	No (265) 56·4%	
If necessary for his affairs	(121) 25·8%		
Only if his soul is at stake	(1) 0·2%		
Unclassified	(27) 5·7%		

Further studies reveal that far more patients are desirous of learning the truth than is sometimes thought. A recent G.A.P. (Group for the Advancement of Psychiatry) Symposium (No. 11) entitled "Death and Dying: Attitudes of Patient and Doctor", drew an interesting contrast "in comparing studies of physicians and patients as to whether the physician should tell or should not tell the patient he is dying, 66–90 per cent of physicians, depending on the specific study, are in favour of not telling the patient. In opposing vein, 77–89 per cent of the patients want to know. Our outlook as physicians", notes Feifel, "may be too conditioned by the 'healthy' rather than by the seriously ill and the dying" (p. 635). In another recent questionnaire,[2] some thirteen hundred physicians replied with comments to the following questions: "When a diagnosis of cancer is established, (1) do you tell the patient the truth, (2) do you tell the patient something reassuring, (3) do you tell someone else in the family but do not tell the patient?" To (1) 57% replied in the affirmative. To (2) 49% reported that they told the patient something reassuring. The implication here was that both the truth and reassurance were sometimes used. It was also reported that 86% stated that "What is told to the patient must fit the individual case". It was felt by 44% that "the family doctor should always make the decision on what to tell the patient", and by 17% that "patients usually suspect the truth so they might as well be told". One of the significant factors in this research was that to the question, "If you had a malignancy would you wish to be told the truth?", 92% of the physicians answered "Yes!" (The physicians under the age of forty were more inclined to reveal the truth to the patient than those who were older.)

Addressing the London Rotary Club in September 1959, Mr A. Dickson Wright, Vice-President of the Royal College of Surgeons, told his audience that those who suffer from cancer should not be told they had the disease, for "it is a thing nobody can stand". Although this is not the same question as telling a patient he is dying, in the correspondence that ensued in *The Times* it was inevitably linked up, and brought out a few interesting features in this very problem. A letter from R. G. C. Jenkins[3] made the following comments:

1. Quite frequently it is not possible for the doctor to hide from his patient the fact that the patient has cancer.

2. Many such patients who know that they have cancer have sufficient spiritual strength to bear this knowledge.

3. Many patients who do not have cancer feel that they have it and fall seriously ill in consequence.

4. If Mr Dickson Wright's recommendation be followed, this is the sort of situation which will become common. A patient with an incurable cancer has his medical adviser, his daughter and two or three relatives around his bed. They tell him (contrary to the truth) that he has no cancer. In consequence the patient may well go to his end a happier man. But a year later the daughter suggests that she also has cancer. Again the doctor tells her that she has no cancer. But the daughter then remembers that the doctor told an untruth to her father and follows with the thought, "Is he not now telling me an untruth also?"

5. The big query arising out of Mr Dickson Wright's suggestion is therefore that in the long run confidence will completely disappear between doctor and patient, because in time patients will learn by experience of the kind given above that doctors do not tell the truth in certain circumstances.

Point 4 of Mr Jenkins' letter is further demonstrated by Walter C. Alvarez, Emeritus Consultant of the Mayo Clinic:[4] "When I am dealing with an elderly person with a functional trouble, I cannot cheer him and reassure him as I would like to do because he is so sure that if he had a cancer I wouldn't tell him about it. And why should I expect him to believe me when for forty years he has watched doctors telling cheerful lies to his dying relatives and friends? Why should he, when he is seriously ill, think that we of the medical profession are going to treat him any differently?"

A further letter in *The Times,* this time from Robert Platt, President of the Royal College of Physicians,[5] emphasized other points,

> In my view [states the writer] patients fall into three categories:
>
> 1. Those who wish to face the facts should be allowed to do so.
> 2. Those who really know the truth but prefer not to discuss it either (a) to avoid embarrassment to the doctor, or (b) because they prefer not to have their fears confirmed and would rather be left with a chink of hope.
> 3. Those who do not want to face the facts and are often patently trying to conceal the truth from themselves (and often from the doctors).
>
> I hope [continues Sir Robert] that if my time comes I will be allowed to be in group 1. If not, I will have to adopt the tactics of 2 (a) for the sake of my doctor's peace of mind.

Kelly and Freisen[6] found that 89 out of 100 cancer patients and 82 out of 100 non-cancer patients said that they preferred to know the truth about their condition. Of a group of 740 healthy people getting a routine yearly physical examination, 98.5% said they wanted to be told, should they develop cancer. We are then told that "the doctors concluded from this research that patients want to be informed of the nature of their illness to a far greater extent than the average physician would anticipate". We find similar conclusions reached from further research undertaken with 101 patients by Gerle, Lunden, and Sandblom:[7] "It may be said that the personality and environment of the individual patient have been shown by the present study to be the factors of decisive importance when considering what to tell the patient with inoperable cancer. There are a small number of patients for whom telling the truth would be an act of needless cruelty. On the other hand, the large number of positive reactions shows that the impact need by no means be an overwhelming shock, and that it may even be of positive value to the patient during the further course of the disease."

So often a conspiracy of silence is maintained which results only in suspicion and deceit all round, and makes the patient more anxious, resentful, and full of self-pity. We have a dramatic illustration in Tolstoy's *The Death of Ivan Ilych* (p. 137f).[8] What tormented Ivan Ilych most

> was the deception, the lie, which for some reason they all accepted, that he was not dying but was simply ill, and that he only need keep quiet and undergo a treatment and then something very good would result. He however knew that do what they would nothing would come of it, only still more agonising suffering and death. This deception tortured him—their not wishing to admit what they all knew and what he knew, but wanting to lie to him concerning his terrible condition, and wishing and forcing him to participate in that lie. Those lies—lies enacted over him on the eve of his death and destined to degrade this awful solemn act ... were a terrible agony for Ivan Ilych. And strangely enough, many times when they were going through their antics over him he had been within a hairbreadth of calling out to them: "Stop lying! You know and I know that I am dying. Then at least stop lying about it!" But he never had the spirit to do it.... This falsity around him and within him did more than anything else to poison his last days.

Ivan realizes his true state, so do all the members of his family, but all are attempting to convince him that his illness is not serious. The result is that Ivan's sense of loneliness is increased, and a feeling of humiliation overcomes him.

Many patients seem to have their end surrounded in mystery and deception with little or no opportunity to prepare for "a good death", and no time to put their worldly goods in order. We cannot all face death in the manner of St Francis of Assisi: "During the summer a doctor from Arezzo came to see him and the saint asked him how long he had to live. The doctor hedged, but at last said that he thought Francis would die at the end of September or early October. On hearing this Francis spread out his hands to the Lord with very great devotion and reverence, and said with great joy of mind and body: 'Welcome, Sister Death'."[9] Few are as prepared as was Pope John XXIII: "...I am ready to take the great journey. My trunks are packed. I can go at any time..." To many a patient we have to recall silently the words of our Lord, "I have many things to say to you, but you cannot bear them now."

There are, however, probably far more patients than we sometimes realize who would prefer to know. A nagging fear together with a dwindling hope is often far harder to bear than the thought of impending death. As Dr Cicely Saunders puts it, "It is my opinion that for many fear of the unknown is harder to bear than fear of the known."[10] When the veil of mystery is lifted, albeit but a little, everyone is freer, for no one has to remember what was last said in order to keep up the pretence. The family can now speak freely about mutual concerns, and the priest is no longer inhibited in his approach with prayer and sacrament. "The strain is surely increased beyond measure", wrote Tizard[11] during the last four months of his life, when his wife had broken the news to him, "if you have always to be on guard lest you betray, by a word or a look, your knowledge that your loved one is not going to get better, keeping up, always, a feigned cheerfulness in his presence, and gaily discussing plans which you know can never be fulfilled. And then, perhaps when hope deferred has made the heart sick, a chilling doubt begins to stir within the sufferer's mind and he is compelled to face the truth when his vitality is at a low ebb and he is less able to grapple and come to terms with it. Better far to know, and face it together". It is debatable whether any member of a family can successfully conceal from the patient the thought of his impending death. It requires great skill to act out a lie, and to continue to be oneself in the midst of deceit. The strain that such predicament imposes upon the member of a family is illustrated by two quotations taken from the remarks of two widows who were interviewed by Geoffrey Gorer in his recent study.[12]

"I knew he was dying", said one, "but he didn't.... It was terrible having to lie to him.... I was abrupt with him sort of, or I would have broke down." The other was stricken with much guilt as a result of concealment. Her husband had been ill with cancer for some 22 months. "I knew, but he didn't ... It was a great strain.... Now I think: 'Did I do right not to tell him?' ... It's very difficult, and you think after if you did right. He used to ask me if he was going to get well, and I often wonder if I did right. My doctor said *he* wasn't going to tell him, and the hospital wouldn't either; so if I tell him, he's not going to have much faith in the hospital, is he? It's just one of those things. I told him awful lies."

Gorer tells us that these two informants are typical of many, and that "what had been good marriages were reduced to unkindness or falsity by the doctor's professional unwillingness to tell his patient the truth. It would obviously be harrowing for a doctor to have to do so, and it is understandable that they share the British fear of the display of emotion; but it would seem worth considering whether this practice is not causing avoidable misery." In *A Very Easy Death* Simone de Beauvoir reveals her feelings as she sat at the bedside of her mother who is dying of cancer. "My unfair harshness wrung my heart. At the time the truth was crushing her and when she needed to escape from it by talking, we were condemning her to silence; we forced her to say nothing about her anxieties and to suppress her doubts; as it had so often happened in her life, she felt both guilty and misunderstood" (p. 66). When honesty has been exercised all through a happily married life, can a husband or wife be expected to enact a drama of silent conspiracy?[13]

The medical world is sometimes prone to justify its silence on humanitarian grounds, that it is kinder for the patient not to know the truth. In many instances, this can so often create a false relationship between doctor and patient.

"There are many patients who value truth in communication," write Hackett and Weisman, "and who will lose confidence as soon as trust is violated. The dying patient needs communication and exchange with those around him more desperately than do other types of patients. Dying is lonely, and closeness and warmth are the only remedies. This is our principal reason for advocating truth."[14]

It is also a deception of the patient at the hour of his greatest need. The doctor in whom he has put his utmost faith and trust now appears to be letting him down. Sometimes this silence can be a mere rationalization of the doctor's unwillingness to face the fact of death, and consequently the easier and simpler course of avoidance is carried through.

Again, it seems taken for granted that the patient has not the moral and spiritual courage to face the fact of death.[15] Every patient should be told *what he really wants to know*, and what he wants to know should be clear to the perceptive and experienced eye of the doctor or nurse. It should never be right to tell deliberate lies, for every man has a right to learn the true facts about his future and about so important a practical and spiritual factor as his imminent death. It is just here that the faith of the doctor has a distinct contribution to make, for "if he does not see anything beyond the death of the body, or if all that he sees is a vague hope that all will be well, then he is really not quali-

fied to judge in this question at all and had better leave the
decision to the relations and the chaplain. But if he is a
Christian, if he believes in the Gospel of our Lord, if the
truth of that Gospel is part of his own experience, then he
will be able to judge faithfully."[16]

To those of us who have the privilege of serving the sick,
it is always surprising how very few patients ask the direct
question, "Am I going to die?" As Dr Glyn Hughes ob-
serves,[17] it is usually framed the other way, if asked at all—
"Am I going to get better?" Even when faced with the
direct question, we must be as aware as possible of the
motive with which it is asked. Often it does not warrant a
real desire to know the truth, but rather seeks for reassurance. If we are convinced that the patient really wants to
know the truth in order to prepare spiritually and arrange
his affairs, the priest or doctor must not hesitate to give it.[18]

By whom is the verdict given? Probably by the person—
be he doctor, priest, nurse, husband, or wife—who is in
closest touch with the patient. It can, of course, be shared
by those who have been caring most for the various needs
of the patient, but it is always better if the solemn duty falls
to one person. Some wise words of Archbishop Anthony
Bloom come to mind here: "I would put as a first, absolute
condition that the person who is going to speak to the dying
must be prepared to remain with this person as long as
necessary—for hours and days. If it is a friend, it must be
the closest; if it is a relative, the kind of relative who is
capable of doing this, and not simply a relative according
to the Table of Kindred; the 'nearest' number One from
that. It must not be a functional thing: the priest, the nurse,
or the doctor. It must be someone chosen because this person
is prepared to do it; and it can be done. . . ."[19]

How is the verdict to be given? Let there be a gradual
leading up to the truth, rather than a "cold-shower" technique, as one patient put it. Such news must be imparted
"with grace and truth". "Glib answers no one has," writes
Gerald J. Aronson,[20] "but I think we must be guided by the

principle of permitting and helping the patient to keep up as much as possible the rôle that is important to him." To carry this out effectively he suggests four rules:

1. Do not tell the patient anything which might induce psychopathology. One is guided here, he suggests, by the "clinical feel and the response of the patient to your comments and manner as you have been slowly going along with him in the course of his illness".

2. Hope must never die too far ahead of the patient.

3. The gravity of the situation should not be minimized. ... The patient will not fail to understand from your demeanour that his situation is serious. ... More good deaths are spoiled because the physician tries to jolly the patient or neglect him as a sentient being!

4. Telling the patient about his impending death in such a way as to avoid just idly sitting around, awaiting death. You must try to estimate the duration of a man's psychological present.

If we are to tell the patient, let it be done in simple clear statements which generate calm and confidence. Otherwise, "the truth you speak doth lack gentleness and time to speak it in; you rub the sore, when you should bring the plaster".[21] Let the telling be as honest as possible, avoiding all unnecessary information, and answering with tact only the particular question asked.

This is a real testing-time for doctor, priest, and family—whoever has been delegated to break the news. Dr Cicely Saunders relates how she once told one of her patients the truth in reply to a direct question. "When I gave it to him," she writes, "he said, 'Was it hard for you to tell me that?' When I said 'Well—yes, it was', he said simply, 'Thank you, it is hard to be told, but it is hard to tell too—thank you'." Commenting on this, Dr Saunders continues, "His answer shows that it should be hard, and that if it is not, we should hesitate about telling the truth. It should be hard because the situation demands all that we have of understanding;

that we may know the right moment and tell the patient in the right way; because we should care very much that this person should do well with what we give him, and also because we are, thereby, committing ourselves to helping him every way we can right up to the end."[22] A moving and dramatic account of breaking the news to a dying patient (in this case a young girl of fifteen) is described for us in *Margaret*,[23] which is a true and heroic account of a young and attractive girl suffering and eventually dying from cancer. After the author tells Margaret that the tumour they had operated on had been malignant, the following reactions are described.

> "You mean I'm going to die?" "Yes, darling, I mean that you're going to die." In the five minutes which followed Margaret went through several rigidly defined phases and, I implicitly believe, received that intangible, dismissed by so many as myth, the Holy Spirit.... I saw a fifteen-year-old girl, whom I loved very dearly, know she had received the ultimate warrant, and sadness, joy, life and agelessness were all in her eyes. Never shall I forget that moment, it will live with me eternally. Many people say that I look younger since it is all over, but that night, in that moment, I aged more than anyone will ever know.... Now she knew the truth and there would be no more deceit, no more undercurrent of tension, she could relax and be perfectly happy with us.

When is the verdict to be given? Such information, if it is to be imparted, should be given at a time when the patient can do something about it, rather than at a final stage when he is powerless to react or make the necessary preparations. Yet it is kinder not to break the news too early, particularly if the illness appears to be progressive and long drawn out. If the period of anticipation is prolonged, the situation becomes extremely painful and distressing for both patient and family. Blessed indeed is he who can talk unemotionally and calmly about death at such a time, for he it is who will emanate confidence and self-surrender within an atmosphere of love and devotion.

Doctors, and priests too (particularly if they serve as hospital chaplains), are able to recount cases which were previously given up as "hopeless" or "incurable", and miracles of recovery have occurred. It is therefore most important that the flame of hope should not be completely extinguished, particularly if the "will to live" is strong in the mind of the patient. Sir Heneage Ogilvie once described "optimism" as the "greatest analgesic, hope, the most certain tranquilliser". Lecturing to newly qualified doctors, Oliver Wendell Holmes issued this warning: "I think I am not the first to utter the following caution—Beware how you take away hope from any human being. Nothing is clearer than that the merciful Creator intends to blind most people as they pass down into the dark valley."

When matters are discussed openly in such an atmosphere, relationships can be genuine and honest. In her article, "Prelude to Death",[24] Jeanette Wilcox described what this meant to both her husband and herself.

> I told him simply and gently that the doctor had used every known resource of science but none had been effective. Then he admitted that he had felt for some time that he was not improving but had been struggling against acknowledging it, even to himself, and had been determined to conceal his innermost fears from me. Here we were, the two of us more deeply in love than I had ever imagined two could be, both trying vainly to carry on alone, when our hearts were nearly breaking. There was deep gratitude in his voice when he thanked me for sharing with him the knowledge that he could not be with me for very long. Pain would be much easier to bear, he added, now that he knew the truth, than it had been during the tedious months of wonder and uncertainty. His one request was that we spend all our time together, that we drink fully of our cup of happiness as long as we could.

Truth does not altogether cancel out hope, neither is hope denied when the prognosis is unfavourable.

Often we shall find that the defence mechanism of "denial" comes into its own during terminal illness, and

there will be many patients who seem to deny the fact of
their condition, although this may be obvious to all around
them. Patients who are in an emaciated condition and pro-
gressively deteriorating will often talk about what they in-
tend to do as soon as they leave hospital, and discuss future
plans in a seemingly optimistic manner. Dr Kenneth Walker,
a former Hunterian Professor of the Royal College of Surgeons, confessed that he had "often been surprised at the
skill displayed by an otherwise intelligent and observant
patient in avoiding how ill he is. Carefully shunning any
direct inquiry about the severity of his disease and dismiss-
ing as irrelevant all signs of an ominous nature, he manages
to continue viewing everything connected with his illness in
a favourable light. Outwardly at any rate he appears to be
entirely ignorant of the truth, but . . . it may well be that
deep within themselves some of these apparently optimistic
patients do realize the fact that their days on earth are
numbered."[25] Some will be convinced that the doctor's
diagnosis must be wrong, and are tossed to and fro between
hope and despair. On the one hand, they tend to see the
optimism of those about them, and on the other, they sense
that there are symptoms of death. While realizing that they
are dying they seem to repudiate the fact of death. "We
rarely find him [i.e. the dying man] looking death in the
face and knowing it is death", wrote Lord Horder. "He is
either very dubious that death is coming to *him*, or his
apperception is so dimmed . . . that the end of life is a
dream-state rather than a true awareness."[26] We are told
that this natural urge to hope and deny is also evident
among prisoners who have been sentenced to death. While
aware of their sentence there is the hope of a last-minute
reprieve (see Appendix).

Often the dying themselves will want to withdraw and
pass through a phase which has become known as the "bereavement of the dying", for a "little death" is already
taking place. The thought of severing all human relationships and losing all he holds dear in life has created in the

dying person a grief reaction analogous to the anticipatory grief of his family and friends.

Many a patient will ask the chaplain or nurse, or even the ward-maid, "Do you think I'm going to get better?" yet not ask the doctor at all. There may be a variety of reasons for this. The relationship between doctor and patient may be so threatening that "death" or "dying" find difficult verbal expression. It may be that they do not feel close enough to the doctor, or have failed to build up a trustful and confident attitude towards him. Again, they may be afraid of a final verdict, or of hearing the true facts of the case, and therefore long for reassurance from others. Writing in the *Journal of Pastoral Care*[27] on "A Study of Terminal Cancer Patients", the Reverend Robert Reeves, Chaplain of the Presbyterian Hospital, New York, reports on the pastoral care of twenty patients who eventually died of cancer. He has some interesting observations to report, for he states that

in the thirteen cases where the patient spoke of death to the chaplain, not a single one indicated that he had mentioned the subject of death to the doctor, or the doctor to him.... Here is an area of the patient's experience in which he feels that we [i.e. the chaplain] belong in a way that no one else appears to.... doctors avoided the subject of death, maintained with the patients the fiction that they were going to get better, did not let them knowingly meet the last great experience of life. Why?—could it be that they, along with most of the rest of us in our world today, have lost their sense of the hereafter, and are afraid? ... I do know this: that the two patients who were permitted to know when they were about to die met death bravely, not quite with banners flying, but with serenity and dignity, as befits a child of God. And I am sure that some of the others among the twelve who showed over-all positive movement toward acceptance would have done the same, had they been allowed to do so. But I cannot prove it statistically!

We have seen that it is impossible to lay down set rules as to whether the dying are to be told or not. It is not ours to prejudge and make decisions for the dying, in whose

5

situation it is impossible to place ourselves. What we have
observed is that probably far more patients would welcome
the truth than is sometimes imagined. Writing of "The
Attitudes Towards Death in some Normal and Mentally Ill
Populations", Dr Herman Feifel emphasizes the help that
dying patients receive when given the opportunity to discuss
their situation. "I think", states the writer, "that one of the
serious mistakes we commit in treating terminally ill
patients is the erection of a psychological barrier between
the living and the dying. Some think and say it is cruel and
traumatic to talk to dying patients about death. Actually,
my findings indicate that patients want very much to talk
about their feelings and thoughts about death, but feel that
we, the living, close off the avenues for their accomplishing
this. . . . A goodly number of terminally ill patients prefer
honest and plain talk about the seriousness of their illness
from their physicians. . . ."[28] This is proved not only by the
evidence of the recollection left to us by those who have
experienced the valley of the shadow of death, but also by
those of us who have the privilege of ministering at the bed-
sides of the dying, and witnessing patients approach the por-
tals of death with full realization, confidence, and serenity.
"Have you not watched that most lovely of all things", asks
Father E. K. Talbot,[29] "a life which has been secretly,
humbly, interiorly dying day by day, and living, ever living
unto God: so that now Death is a friend leading the soul to
the home and goal which all along has been its home, its
goal, which it has waited for expectantly—the soul which
has looked for and loved his appearing?"

It is not so much *what* is told, but *how* it is told that
matters most. "Personally I think that a quiet straight answer
with a clear look in the eye is as a rule the best reply," suggests W. N. Leak,[30] "and it is usually answered by a quiet,
'Thank you, Doctor,' or 'I knew it'. It is vastly easier to
manage the patient after such a simple and sincere acknow-
ledgement of the fact. And if the doctor can honestly also

speak of that land where 'there is no more death neither sorrow nor crying, neither shall there be any more pain', the last
dying days may be full of hope and peace instead of violent
struggle and despair."

Whether the dying should be told or not becomes less a
problem when we acknowledge that many patients themselves know that they are dying, and truth then becomes a
relationship rather than words. Perhaps the only rule
whereby the doctor may be wisely guided is for him to know
the facts, to know the patient, and to know himself. The
average layman now knows far more about his illness than
perhaps ever before, for his reading of various popular
articles and his viewing of television programmes have
brought many medical facts to his notice as well as breaking
down much of the "mystique" of medicine and surgery. The
real question to be asked is where is this particular patient
at this moment. We must understand that the process of
dying is an ever changing one, and where the dying lead,
we must follow. By our creative listening and understanding, by our acceptance of them, we shall find that our actions speak louder than words and become far more
effective. If we are perceptive and sensitive to their needs, if
we have watched with them through periods of stress and
anxiety and fear, we shall the better understand and re-
spond to their moods. If they wish to talk about their condition, we can encourage them to put their feelings into
words. In other instances it will seem better not to disclose
the true facts.

Whatever their wishes we have to respect them, for it is
never morally right to force the truth upon anyone. It is
not ours to pass death-sentences or to fire point-blank
answers to the questions asked, but neither should we deceive the dying with words of false assurance when they are
searching for the truth. Those who have helped the patient
in his suffering should now be able "to help him to die, to
die well, or more truly to be born again into eternal life".

Appendix

On Sunday 2 August 1964, the B.B.C. broadcast an interview with a former prisoner who had been condemned to death. The programme was entitled *Allowed to Live*. The prisoner recalled his reactions as he awaited his execution in the condemned cell at Wandsworth Prison:

> "I found it very difficult to believe right up to the end that it was me that was there, that it was me that was waiting to be executed. . . . I was afraid I was going to be executed . . . but on the other hand, there was alway a hidden hope shall we say, or a subconscious hope or belief that this was all an act . . . they were trying to frighten me all the time, but in the end they were going to let me go." He was able to appeal to the House of Lords, but this was dismissed. He began to resign himself "to the fact that they were trying to execute me". Yet he could continue, "I wouldn't say I was convinced that this was it. I still had that *one glimmer of hope that I was going to be reprieved and that I was going to be allowed to live*" (italics mine).

He was later reprieved by the Home Secretary and served a life sentence.

H. Bluestone and C. L. McGahee interviewed eighteen men and one woman in the Sing-Sing death house, all of whom had been convicted of murder. The writers reported that "defense mechanisms of denial and projection were effective in warding off anxiety and depression", and that the "second common form of denial is to minimize the gravity of the present situation and to take for granted that *an appeal will be successful*"[31] (italics mine).

We find a similar attitude in Viktor Frankl's *Man's Search for Meaning* [Hodder 1964], p. 83, where the author endeavours to give life a meaning in a concentration camp:

I asked the poor creatures who listened to me attentively in the darkness of the hut to face up to the seriousness of our position. They must not lose hope but should keep their courage in the certainty that the hopelessness of our struggle did not detract from its dignity and its meaning. I said that someone looks down on each of us in difficult hours—a friend, a wife, somebody alive or dead, or a God—and he would not expect us to disappoint him. He would hope to find us suffering proudly—not miserably—knowing how to die.... Nearly everyone in our transport lived under the illusion that he would be reprieved, that everything would yet be well.

4

The Pastoral Care of the Dying

Beside the bed where parting life was laid,
And sorrow, guilt and pain by turns dismayed,
The reverend champion stood. At his control
Despair and anguish fled the struggling soul;
Comfort came down the trembling wretch to raise,
And his last faltering accents whispered praise.

OLIVER GOLDSMITH, *The Deserted Village.*

God be at mine end, and at my departing.

Old Sarum Primer

Lord, now lettest thou thy servant depart in peace ...

St Luke 2.29

More than a century ago Sir Henry Halford described a dying patient thus: "The eyes glazed and half closed, jaw dropped and mouth open, cold and flaccid lip; cold, clammy sweats on head and neck; respirations shallow or slow and stertorous with rattle; pulse irregular, unequal, weak and immeasurably fast; prostrate on back, arms tossing in disorder, hands waved languidly before the face or grasping through empty air, fumbling with bedclothes...."[1] But if we should add to-day "housed in oxygen tent and harassed by tubes", we can be thankful that by means of modern techniques and drugs the end will most likely be calmer and less disturbing.[2]

Few would say that they really felt at ease in the presence of the dying patient, for there is a certain awe and mystery, a certain uneasiness, which overcomes one. This note finds illustration in a poem by Mary C. Gillington entitled "A Dead March":

> Be hushed, all voices and untimely laughter;
> Lest one least word be lightly said
> In the awful presence of the dead.[3]

Even in hospital where death occurs frequently it is often seen as an embarrassment.[4]

> The surgeon is superstitious [writes Cappon].[5] He needs to be optimistic and shut out twinges of professional guilt and worry. He turns away. The physician feels impotent. Though sympathetic, he turns away. The psychiatrist faces often the threat of man turned against himself; but if suicide is carried through, the psychiatrist also looks away, covered in guilt and shame. Even the priest absorbs his keenest feelings in rituals. The relatives and friends are immersed and blinded by grief; the nurses busy; only the poet and philosopher takes a look from afar.

"Death is no stranger to me", writes another. "As a doctor, I have often seen men dying, and I have often seen men dead. Still, the drama of death never ceases to be grievous and disquieting."[6]

Before we can minister effectively to the dying we have to come to terms with the meaning of our own dying, for not until we ourselves have worked out fully the purpose of life and the meaning of its end can we hope to be of assistance to those who find themselves "in the valley of the shadow". At each deathbed, doctor, priest, nurse, and family come face to face with their own departure, and must be prepared and ready to answer such questions as, "Whence came I?", "Whither go I?" Death can never be a private matter, for each death reminds us of our own. "Any man's death diminishes me, because I am involved in mankind; And therefore never send to know for whom the bell tolls; it tolls for thee."[7]

Unless we ourselves are reconciled to death, we may unconsciously avoid a meaningful relationship with the dying, for "when a patient begins to die, he is hard to love" (Wahl). We are liable to become no more than Job's comforters (Job 13.5,13: "O that ye would altogether hold your peace! and it should be your wisdom. . . . Hold your peace, let me alone, that I may speak, and let come on me what will.") A dying person was once asked what he looked for above all in the people who were caring for him. "For someone to look as if they were trying to understand me", he remarked. "He did not ask for success, but only that someone should care enough to try", comments Dr Cicely Saunders.[8]

We shall find that to many a patient the depression and weariness which often accompany the last illness may be far more irksome and hard to bear than his physical pain and discomfort. As was noted in a previous chapter, he greatly fears loneliness and abandonment. Archbishop Anthony Bloom once told a Conference of Hospital Chaplains:

One of the tragic things I find in the West is the gradual loneliness in which a dying person is secluded. The person knows, in body and in soul, that death is coming, but the husband smiles, the daughter smiles, the nurse smiles, and the doctor smiles, and everyone smiles, in such a way that the patient knows it is a lie, because—goodness—people have a heart; are sensitive to one another. And the result is that if there is distress, it is to be faced in a lonely way: if there is fear: if there is hope: if there is despair: if there is need for the help of a priest, even at that point it will snap, because the priest is also part of the conspiracy. While if the things have been spoken of then there are so many things which you do not need to say . . . the person who has spoken is the one who is prepared to go all the way and not just "hit and run". I think that there is a whole education that we must undertake with regard to families, and to clergy, and to doctors, and to nurses, because it cannot be a functional thing . . . we are not there to make it impossible for people to go through a physical experience that has moral content: or through a spiritual experience that is the very process of growth into eternity; not into the void of which people are afraid, but into the fullness of life which makes it possible for people not to see any void, and to be fulfilled....[9]

Apart from relief of pain, security and companionship are the primary needs of the dying. Often he helps most who is ready to listen. There is passive listening which can be used when stress is great, and the dying one anxious to talk about his fear and frustrations. There is active or directed listening which perhaps calls for even greater skill, and is coupled with the art of asking questions and so encouraging the patient to talk, if this should be found helpful and necessary. We have to watch for hints that he may want to talk about the future, for he can then be encouraged to put into words his feelings and anxieties. So many will want to help him forget, or pretend he is getting along well, whereas what he really needs is encouragement to remember, and so express his fears of death. If these are continually repressed the patient is not being enabled to work through his sense of abandonment and emotional deprivation.

A sense of guilt is often present, together with a feeling of self-disappointment. There are many tasks unfinished, many hopes remain unfulfilled. There will be sadness at the thought of leaving behind those one has held dear, and a sense of frustration leads to further anxiety. Another "strongly pronounced component of the dying patient's fear of death", notes Rosenthal, "may be the awareness of losing his power over his destiny. The more dominant, the more aggressive the individual was in the past, the stronger will be his fear of death. A rebel in life is a rebel in death. Just as he did not submit in life, so he does not yield in death without in-tensive struggle. Conversely, the man who has always been submissive and humble, or was fatalistically resigned to the demands of living, is better prepared to face death, to give up his life with less of a fight and even with less fear."[10] A few patients express resentment, which can be directed into various channels. "So much for this hospital and its staff!" "Why is this happening to me? I've always lived a good life and done my best." There are some patients who, religiously speaking, tend to bargain with God. "If you will grant my life, I will do thus and so...." "When bargaining fails, bitterness may descend upon the soul until there comes a feeling of 'Thy Will be done'. After this the patient is at peace and seems able to meet death with quiet courage."[11]

At the bedside of the dying, both Church and Medicine must stand complementary one to the other, for materialism has very little to offer in such circumstances. Indeed, Lord Fisher of Lambeth goes so far as to say that "when it comes to dying, there is no distinction between doctor and chaplain—both are pastors, and the faith of the doctor can often do far more than that of the chaplain, just because the doctor has been fighting the battle of life and death with the patient day by day more intimately than can often be the case for the chaplain".[12] Worcester, too, seems to bear this out when he writes that "the dying do not always recognize the difference between the clerical and medical professions. They seem also unable to recognize the difference between the need for physical relief and that of consolation."[13]

If he exercises his art aright, sees the patient as a person who has placed the utmost trust and confidence in him, the doctor's ministry closely approximates that of the priest, but of course can never be a substitute for it. At present there is urgent need for far more mutual discussion between the two professions on the ministry to the dying, for both are concerned with the needs of the whole man. It surely cannot be right to adopt an oversimplified distinction of the physical needs being solely directed to the doctor, and the spiritual to the priest, for the two are inseparable. "It is not *any* living body, as if it were that of an animal, which the doctor must attend: it is a human body. It is not a pure spirit with which the priest must deal, but the spirit of a man which exercises itself, which expresses itself through his body."[14] Those who have been trained to minister to the needs of people in life are not always adequately trained to meet the needs of those nearing death.

As a member of the Body of Christ each partner in the healing team has a distinct contribution to make, and we shall now attempt to outline the ministry of (1) the doctor, (2) the nurse, (3) the family, (4), the social worker, and (5) the priest, as each seeks together to bring comfort and consolation to those who are about to die. Each has his different methods of approach; each his separate rôle to fulfil, but all have to employ particular defence-mechanisms, for far more of oneself is exposed in this encounter than probably in any other relationship.

THE DOCTOR

"I observe the Phisician with the same diligence as hee the disease; I see hee feares, and I feare with him. . . . I feare the more, because he disguises his feare, and I see it with the more sharpnesse, because hee would not have me see it."[15] An over-busy doctor who has little time to devote to his patients will not inspire the dying with that trust and confidence which are so much needed to create an atmosphere of calm and serenity, for "in the practice of our [i.e. the doctor's] art it matters little what medicine is given, but matters much that we give ourselves with our pills".[16] Although it is obviously important that he does not become emotionally entangled in the strains and stresses of his patient, it is nevertheless equally if not more important that the doctor cultivates more than a mere physiological interest in, and concern for, his patient. A wholly impersonal approach does not encourage a spirit of trust and confidence in the patient which is so necessary for mutual goodwill. Writing on "Reflections on Ageing and Death" in the *Lancet*, 5 January 1963, Sir Robert Platt emphasizes the relationship between doctor and patient in such circumstances.

More opportunity should be given for such discussions if the patient indicates a wish for them. Far too often he falls into the mutual conspiracy of silence, for if his first approaches are met with an immediate rebuff by the doctor who brushes

aside all likelihood of a fatal outcome, the patient is not encouraged to express his fears or discuss his feelings. He keeps
them privately to himself, but the doctor is mistaken if he
thinks his superficial reassurances are accepted. He has merely
given the patient the impression that the voicing of his most
intimate thoughts and fears will be unwelcome.

Being brought face to face with his dying patient can be
a most threatening and frustrating experience for the doctor. Eissler attempts to explain this in the following terms:
"The spirit of doing, controlling, combatting and destroy-
ing diseases is probably a great impediment to the understanding and study of death. Therefore it is not surprising
that medicine has contributed so little. In view of death
there is nothing to do, to control, to combat, or to destroy
... the man of medicine knows well how to describe a sickness, its symptoms, its causes, and its termination, but death
is for him something negative, a deficit, the absence of
something."[17] Viktor Frankl describes it thus: "A doctor
who is sensitive to the imponderables of a situation will always feel a kind of shame when attending a patient with an
incurable disease, or a dying person. For the doctor himself
is helpless, incapable of wresting his victim from death.
But the patient has become a hero who is meeting his fate
and holding his own by accepting it in tranquil suffering.
That is, upon a metaphysical plane, a true achievement—
while the doctor in the physical world, in his physician's
realm, has his hands tied, is a failure."[18] He must not therefore be too troubled by disappointment or failure, for otherwise he will be eager to withdraw as soon as he possibly can
and reject the whole situation. This can readily be sensed
by the patient and his sense of abandonment made more
acute. Often the normal procedure appears to be that given
in *The Practitioner*, August 1948, which advises that, "when
there is no longer any hope of recovery, but plans have been
made for nursing and the relief of symptoms, there is an art
in allowing the relatives to take charge while the doctor
recedes into a more secondary position". This view has been

severely challenged by another medical writer who contends that "this attitude is defeatist when it should be defiant, for death defied reveals, as nothing else can do, the dignity and power of man's unconquerable soul. . . . The doctor retires when the patient may need him most. He summons the relatives, tells them there is no more he can do, then washes his hands and retires. An attitude so reminiscent of Pontius Pilate when he was manoeuvred into a false position by importunate Jews. Although he knew what justice demanded he could not face up to the awkwardness of seeing that it was done."[19]

When the patient faces a terminal state, it is important that he should realize that something is being done; that he is not merely being passed by or overlooked, and that everything possible is done to relieve his pain. Stressing the importance of this in the care of cancer patients, Ogilvie[20] states that "the value of injections in the treatment of patients dying of carcinoma is inexpressible, because 'a course of injections' is associated in most minds with modern therapeutics, with drugs of strange potency, and with a plan of treatment spread over a long period and requiring many weeks to produce a recognizable effect. The injection need not be given more than once a week, but that weekly 'prick', administered with due ceremony, means treatment, hope, belief that something is being done. . . ." When pain becomes intense, few doctors would hesitate in administering drugs for its alleviation, although perhaps these same drugs may incur the risk of hastening death by their application. This of course is an entirely different matter from deliberately ending the patient's life and so practising euthanasia. His primary goal should always be to assuage the fear of death and of the process of dying in the patient, helping him to die well with dignity and hope of eternal life.[21]

If the doctor believes in the gospel of the hereafter he can bring much to his ministry with the dying, for the question

"Am I going to die?" can often lead on to another, "Is there a life after death?" If he has no answer to the second he will always be tempted to avoid the first. Standing as the representative of Him who came "to heal the brokenhearted, and preach deliverance to the captives, and set at liberty them that are bruised", he can "give back to a man who has lost it the meaning of his moral life, if not in clear fashion, at least in the awakening of a conscience until then distracted or clouded. It is not our province to study the discipline which imposes on the doctor such a conception of his life as a doctor, and the culture which it demands; let it suffice for us to indicate the grandeur which it will confer on his personal life and the splendour to which that life will attain."[22]

Summing up the physician's rôle in terminal illness, Paul S. Rhoads gives the following advice to his colleagues.

Ours is not an ecclesiastical priesthood and we should never attempt to make it so, but it is a priesthood of a sort, nonetheless—one for which medical school has not prepared us. To be prepared for it, somehow each of us must, in his own way, have searched for meaning in his daily tasks. Whether he considers himself religious in the conventional sense or not, he must have given some consideration to the universe in which he lives, to the place of man in it, and to the force or mind or God—call it what you will—behind it all ... How he will act in this exquisitely personal relationship will depend upon how we see ourselves in this mighty scheme of things. If, as our religion teaches, there is a touch of the divine in every man—and what perceptive physician who has seen the heroism with which ordinary people meet the greatest calamities can doubt it?—the greatest satisfaction we can derive is in helping to unlock the resources that are there to meet the challenge of terminal illness. Our task is not to speak of heaven or to be the father confessor, unless the patient chooses to place us in this role. Our task is, rather, to be a friend who is aware of the road ahead and is willing to go along that road with the patient, trusting that the human spirit is too precious for the dissolution of the body to be its final event.[23]

There is at present very little communication between doctors and priests on the subject of their mutual ministry to the dying and bereaved, neither does there appear to be adequate preparation throughout the training of the medical student on the care of the dying and a study of the psychological processes involved.[24] In a paper given at the 3rd World Congress of Psychiatry, 8 June 1961 at Montreal, on "The Physician's Management of Death and the Dying Patient", Charles W. Wahl stressed that the "most necessary precondition in the management of the terminally ill is that the physician have the willingness and capacity to look deeply within himself not only to scrutinize his attitudes towards living and dying, and some of the unconscious equivalences of the latter, but also to consider what might be called the eternal questions ... and derive from them in terms of his own needs and understanding, answers that are meaningful and significant for himself".

THE NURSE

To the young nurse a death on the ward, especially during the silent hours of the night when probably there are fewer senior staff around her, can be a very traumatic experience as well as a testing of her faith. The Christian nurse must be ready to give answers to various questions which might be asked by the patients, and where necessary refer them to either the sister or the doctor. If she feels over-anxious and insecure the nurse will always be tempted to turn the conversation into more favourable channels by avoiding the real issues involved [See Appendix 3]. At such a time her conversation should be patient-centred, for she must not be sidetracked into offering glib answers. When a patient asks, "Nurse, do you think I am going to die?" she will attempt to find out why such a question has been prompted. What does "dying" or "death" mean to this patient at this particular moment? The patient must be helped to express his anxieties with his nurse, whose whole bearing should convey calm and assurance. Little help is given by the nurse who merely expresses her own feelings by promptly changing the subject—"O you mustn't be morbid and think of such things!"; by moralizing—"Well, we are all dying really!"; by denying—"Of course not!"; by philosophizing—"I could walk out and be killed on the road. No one knows when their time comes!" Such efforts only block further communication, and the patient is left in an anxious and tense state. If the nurse becomes embarrassed no patient—above all, the dying—will talk freely of his major concerns.

Wherever possible, she should stay at the bedside at the moment of death, for what Ogilvie says of the doctor is equally applicable to the nurse. "Almost the greatest service the doctor can offer the dying man is to give him the assurance that he will be with him to the end, still holding his hand as he steps out on to the ferry."[25] In the loneliness of death as the props fall away "prior to the gliding of the craft into another element", the clasp of an outstretched hand assuages much of the fear of dying, and gives the patient who sees this as a normal gesture the assurance that there is one who is prepared to watch by him at this hour. Dr Frederick Wertham, author of *The Seduction of the Innocent*, recalls how physical touch helped him during the time of an operation. "I remember only two factors", he records, "which alleviated my general feeling of insecurity while on the operating table. One was the voice of the operating surgeon and one was the reassurance derived from definite physical contact ... words spoken by medical friends present ... had relatively little helping effect. But physical contact did have.... Evidently friendly physical contact of this primitive type is not sufficiently recognized as a helpful procedure." A patient may see himself as "abhorrent" or "untouchable", and physical contact does much to calm a disturbed reaction such as this. Sitting close to him, holding his hand, the nurse gradually bridges the chasm between the living and the dead.

In a sociologist's analysis of the preparation of professional nurses in Canadian hospitals and their attitude to death,[26] the following reactions were recorded. Nine out of the twenty-one nurses interviewed stated that they were eventually able to adjust satisfactorily by gradually adopting a more impersonal attitude to it, even when the initial death has been upsetting. Twelve found it very difficult to face, and for some, death was still an upsetting experience. One nurse comments as follows: "Death is still very disturbing to me. It is one thing I have never been able to accept. As soon as a patient dies, I become upset. This is particularly true in the case of babies or young people. Many disturbing thoughts enter my mind, such as, 'If there is a God, why does he let this happen'?"[27] Some nurses found it difficult to hide their emotions and "play the poised impersonal rôle of a nurse". Others found the physical aspect of death distasteful. "When life has left the body, I am repelled by it. It no longer seems human to me. I perform my duties as quickly as possible and then get away from the situation." A number suffered from a feeling of inadequacy and their inability to hold life back.[28] A programme entitled "The Nurses", broadcast in the B.B.C. World Service, also brought out some interesting features on the problem, "How do young nurses face the death of a patient?"

Nurse A: "It's the one thing that up till now I can't get used to, especially in facing the relatives who are really upset, or in attending to the dead man, it's just terrible."

Nurse B: "You certainly feel a loss and grief—I do personally, I know that."

Nurse C: "You've got to be your usual self to the rest of the patients, and you mustn't let them get depressed by it, and you have to go ahead and clear up, and that's it, sort of thing. But I don't think this is where it ends, you then go home, and you'll probably howl your eyes out for a little bit . . ."

Matron: "I think we can help a nurse a great deal, partly, I think, by encouraging her to talk out her problems with

6

people, and not to be afraid to express her own emotional feelings about them in the normal way."

The more opportunity given to nurses to discuss and express these fears and inadequacies the better, and the chaplain can do much here if he is given opportunity to have discussion groups with his nurses in their introductory course and during their block periods (especially the latter, as the former will have had little experience of ward duties in their early weeks in hospital).[29] In this way the nurse is helped to realize the inevitability of death and to understand a little of its inner meaning. She can also be shown how she can play a major part in the spiritual support of the patient during this critical stage of his illness. Joy Burden relates a tragic and true story illustrating the rôle of the nurse.

> A young woman, not a nurse, sat with a seriously injured girl of thirteen. "I think I am going to die", the child said. "I shan't mind as long as I know I'll be all right—will I be?" Her visitor was so shaken, and also so vague about the Christian belief, that she just could not help her. If only she had assured her of God's love and protection, and said a prayer with her, that girl would have passed on supremely aware of His loving care surrounding her. As it was, she began her last journey in bewildered uncertainty. This kind of situation may sometimes confront you as a nurse. God Himself will equip you spiritually to help patients if you turn to him in faith, and in willingness to be used at this level. . . . At no time is a nurse more effective than on an occasion of this kind.[30]

To nurse a dying patient is both a challenge and an art.[31]

THE FAMILY

In all close relationships there are ambivalent feelings. At the deathbed these can be accentuated, and conflicting emotions often arise. These may lead to a sense of guilt or even subconscious anger. Unless the conflicts are worked through with the chaplain or medical social worker they become intensified and lead to rather shallow and confusing communication with the dying. Such feelings as these need to be accepted, faced, and understood, for "it is difficult for the patient to have a healthy attitude towards dying when those about him are saturated in unhealthy feelings about it".[32]

The loneliness which the dying experiences can be much alleviated by the assurance that his nearest and dearest care, and will be prepared to watch with him as he faces death. Although under certain circumstances it may prove extremely difficult, the members of the family should as far as possible avoid showing signs of extreme distress and sorrow, for the dying can so easily feel a sense of abandonment if the family is too grieved to watch and pray. Even our Lord expressed disappointment in the Garden of Gethsemane when his disciples failed to keep their watch with him. The closer the relationship, the more essential it is that such visits should be frequent and not prolonged, for no good is done by long hours of vigil at the bedside. Short, frequent visits are always preferable, otherwise the members of the family become tired and stressed and transmit their feelings to the patient who is already struggling with his own fears and thoughts.

It is most helpful if the family is told what to expect, as far as it is possible to anticipate, for it can be extremely trying if the patient becomes delirious or disorientated. He may also regress, become selfish and far more demanding than is natural. Such character traits can be unpleasant and disturbing to those who are nearest the patient and not prepared. Some relevant information from the doctor or sister beforehand will make it easier for the family to re-adjust itself to the threatening change of behaviour which might occur.[33]

A feeling of utter helplessness sometimes overcomes the family—there seems very little anyone can do apart from sit and wait, as it were. Although this may be very true from a practical point of view, they can be led to see that there is inward as well as outward activity. The Virgin Mary was not doing nothing although standing helplessly at the foot of the Cross, and not for one moment did her stillness symbolize defeat but intense activity. Comfort is brought to others —especially the dying—by the mere presence of those who love and care. In the quiet and stillness we and our loved ones can rest in the presence of the Holy Spirit, and receive life and power from his hands.

During a long illness and the constant watch at the bedside, with hope mingled with fear, the family may wish that the end might come quickly and all be over so that the loved one might "be spared all this suffering and pain". When death does eventually occur, there might be a sense of guilt resulting from such thoughts. The patient has been "wished away", and they feel in some way responsible. This is but a natural reaction, and it is always helpful for them to have a word with the chaplain, parish priest, or social worker, so that these disturbing feelings might be openly discussed with an understanding, sympathetic, and skilled listener.

Visitors' Rooms in hospitals are not always as bright and light as they might be. Indeed many are rather foreboding and gloomy, symbolizing despair and hopelessness. In order to break the vigil in the ward, advantage might be taken of the hospital chapel, and time can be profitably spent there in quiet prayer and meditation. The chaplain will always be available to help and support those who are so troubled. It has already been noted that many patients die peaceably and calmly, and it is often the family who suffer most. Many must be reassured that Almighty God does not desert them at such a time as this, but is there right in the heart of their pain and sorrow, ready to succour and uplift them. In the words of de Chardin,

> We must overcome death by finding God in it. Christ has conquered death, not only by suppressing its evil effects, but by reversing its sting. By virtue of Christ's rising again, nothing any longer kills inevitably, but everything is capable of becoming the blessed touch of the divine hands, the

blessed influence of the will of God upon our lives. However marred by our faults, or however desperate in its circumstances our position may be, we can, by a total re-ordering, completely correct the world around us and resume our lives in a favourable sense.[34]

THE SOCIAL WORKER

There will be a great deal of overlap between the work of the social worker and that of the priest, for the same emotional strains and stresses will confront both professions. In order that a complete picture be procured of the patient, it rests with the social worker to assemble as much information as possible about the family as a unit. She can help its members to work through the social and psychological problems which face them in their present circumstances. By her casework experience and her counselling technique she can discreetly inquire about the composition of the family and the rôle of the dying patient within it.

The social worker can further explore the avenues of communication within the family group, and see where help is most needed in the reconstruction of the unit. Each member should be given emotional support and guidance for the future, and his guilt and grief worked through. If necessary, the meaning of the illness and the impending death of the patient will be discussed together, and the emotional reactions handled with skill and care.

If the patient wishes to be put in touch with his priest or minister, an immediate contact can be made. Social and financial resources, where necessary, can be planned for those who are in need, be it patient or members of the family. In this way, much solace and peace of mind can be given to those concerned. The specialized skills and insights of the social worker can be used to help the patient meet some of his needs, and his dignity as a human being can be safeguarded. Each patient will naturally vary in social and economic background, as well as in personality and emotional "make-up". Each factor will have to be taken into account, so that the maximum help can be given.

It is essential that the utmost co-operation exists between the doctor, chaplain, and the social worker, so that after mutual discussion each can approach the dying patient with the utmost confidence and competence, avoiding such errors as either saying too much or too little, and causing conflict in a mind and body already disturbed.

If the patient has to return home from hospital, the physical and emotional strengths of those who are to care for him have to be carefully evaluated, and available resources in the National Health Service called upon if needed. The strengths and weaknesses of the marital relationship can be explored, and a real understanding acquired of the various emotional mechanisms employed by both patient and the remainder of the family. These will naturally vary in degree as the illness progresses, and it is of great help if the social worker is sufficiently skilled to anticipate crisis. In this way, members of the family are more prepared to make appropriate readjustments, and impairment of the family unit is kept to a minimum.

Should it be decided to transfer the patient to a "terminal care" home, it is important that a sense of security be given by the social worker explaining "what the future may be following admission to any type of hospital or home if this becomes inevitable, as well as a description of the type of accommodation they are going to, and an assurance that no further change will be required. If this is done by an understanding person, peace and contentment will result, rather than fear, unhappiness and resentment".[35] The social worker will be greatly helped in her ministry to the dying by observing some of the following considerations.[36] She should

1. Understand her own reactions and attitude towards dying and death.
2. Know that feelings of inferiority, inadequacy, dependency, guilt, and rejection are common and sig-

nificant attitudes to these patients (i.e. cancer patients) and that they interfere with optimum adjustment.

3. Accept the hypothesis that whether or not the patient states his feelings he usually knows or suspects the truth of his condition and is reacting to it.

4. Treat the problem of fear and anxiety concerning the diagnosis and prognosis in each case according to the personality and needs of the patient.

5. Help the patient maintain his pattern of defence unless it interferes with his usual course of behaviour and is causing marked disruptions to self and/or family members.

6. Give the patient an opportunity to talk about his illness if he wants to. Let the patient take the lead in any discussion of the diagnosis, and clarify, whenever necessary, any misconceptions by the use of simple, clear statements and by showing interest.

7. Recognize the need for following through with preventive health measures for family members by giving each individual, wherever possible, the opportunity to discuss his relationship with the patient.

8. Offer psychological support that is appropriate to the patient's feelings and the gravity of the situation.

9. Avoid the use of over-simplification, over-reassurance, unnecessary circumlocution, and untruths. Remember that one need not tell the whole truth, but what one says must be truthful.

10. Plan visits regularly and maintain the same degree of interest throughout the period that she is needed by the patient or his family.

THE PRIEST

At the outset it must be said that what the priest *is* at the bedside of the dying is far more effective than what he *says*. His manner must bring calm and serenity; his voice must be quiet and confident, and his whole being bear evidence of one "who has been with Jesus". At all costs, any impression of "over-busyness" must be avoided. Rather, he should sit or stand quietly at the bedside, prepared to stay with the patient for as long as it is deemed necessary.

Although fundamentally his ministry to the dying is very much the same as his general ministry to the sick, the priest will find that in the former special needs have to be met and emotional reactions resolved to a far greater extent than in the latter. Before he can minister adequately to the dying, he must face his own fears and anxieties with respect to death and its encounter. He must be prepared to enter the valley with his patients in fullest sympathy and deepest understanding. His ear must be ready to listen to what information the dying wish to impart, and he must be prepared to share their unresolved problems and their conflicting emotions. This is the paramount time for listening and entering into the deepest silence with his patients—so that "what flows between the minister and the sufferer is prayer of another order". It is as easy for him to hide behind the ritual of the sacraments as it is for the doctor to remain impersonal behind his mask or stethoscope. He can minister the sacraments frequently, and yet at the same time remain aloof from any meaningful relationship or genuine "I–Thou" encounter with the patient. He must rather let these seeming barriers of protection become avenues of approach which lead to shared feelings and helpful communication.

Innumerable questions will be asked of him. "What have I done to deserve this?" "Why does God allow me to suffer in this way?" The priest should always attempt to work through these difficulties with the patient, rather than try to find easy answers couched in familiar clichés or illustrations. There may be a temptation to repress them lest he expose his own inadequacies. Rather he should lead the sufferer to see that there are no simple solutions, for we do not pretend to be able to understand or interpret what the will of God might be. It is not given to man to understand why and how such things happen, but only how, as Chris-

tians, we should meet and face them. Blessed is the priest
who is able to show to the dying that:

> Your death has already been died by Christ whose member
> you are, on the bed of the cross He took it into His. You go
> through your death with Him and into eternal life through
> Him. His death was an oblation, in Him shall yours be this.
> In your body, in the mode of natural existence, you will be
> alone, and it is that condition of lonely separation, of division
> from all other human persons, which holds the wretchedness
> and darkness of death; to be met by the fortitude which is
> yours within the baptismal gifts of faith, hope and love ...
> your spirit is potentially already in God because He is in it,
> your death is a return, and to the act of returning you must
> give yourself with all desire, all energy of will; answering death
> with the ready and joyful assent which, with all humility, you
> have always given to the silver trumpet-call of life's solemn
> occasions, from the font onwards. "Do you?" "I do". "Will
> you?" "I will".[37]

In his book, *The Psychiatrist and the Dying Patient*,
Eissler envies the resources of the priest in his approach to
the dying, for he feels that "the priest or minister is in a
more favourable position [than is the psychiatrist] since he
is a representative of the power beyond, before which the
faithful who is dying believes he will soon appear ... the
psychiatrist ... must first establish a platform which the man
of God finds already made" (p. 247). Although this may be
so, the priest's ministry to the dying is his most difficult yet
most privileged task, for "he seeks to represent the divine
while being human, and would seek to give insight into
the mysteries that are ultimately as mysterious to him as
to others. He would speak of immortality while deeply
aware of his own mortality. He would seek to explain the
meaning of death when he has only conjectures and not
answers."[38] Many a patient will look for the doctor to
arrive and expect to see in him the one who can rescue him
from his present predicament. So often the doctor can
co-operate with the priest, and facilitate his approach to
the patient and make his ministry more effective. The

knowledge that the doctor recognizes the need for spiritual counsel will be of immense importance to the patient.

The availability of the priest will not absolve the doctor from involvement in the emotional and spiritual encounter with the patient, for his approach is often more welcomed than that of "the man of God". Some patients resist such an encounter "because in their minds his intrusion into the scene so definitely betokens the beginning of the last leg of life's journey. To others, with a deep sense of guilt . . . the clergyman, in some vague way, represents divine judgement which the patient is not yet prepared to face."[39] C. S. Lewis in his penetrating book, *The Problem of Pain*, says: "It is safe to tell the pure in heart that they shall see God, for only the pure in heart want to." In a careful study of some twenty patients dying at a general hospital, Cappon can report that "actually there was far more active seeking, without necessarily accepting, for medical information, albeit ominous, than there was for religion. But when religion was sought, the fatal verdict given by medicine was even more actively sought and accepted".[40]

Far too frequently, the priest is not summoned until almost all is over. There is still much prejudice about the very presence of the priest during the final stages of sickness, and the words of Jeremy Taylor have an up-to-date ring about them.[41]

The ministry of the priest should commence before the terminal stage is reached, for a complete stranger arriving on the scene during the final hours can be disconcerting and disturbing to the patient. In cases of emergency or sudden illness where there is little time, this becomes inevitable, but wherever possible a relationship between priest and patient should be built up over the days or weeks by frequent and brief visits. The priest may sometimes be regarded "as being as much a stranger as the wounded Jew in the Gospel regarded the Samaritan", but he must, so to speak, "take hold of the sick man, his brother, and lift him

up in order that he may bring him to the light which enlightens him, and cause him to recognize in the life that is
fading merely the call to a life that is endless, the way to the
beatitude which he has until now vainly striven to em-
brace".[42] What relationship is fostered must be freely
shared. It cannot be forced. The patient "may be a close
friend, a parishioner with deep commitment, or he may be
a complete stranger. He may be an atheist hostile to the
Church or a saint already in communion with God. Whatever the past relationship, one fact is certain: A man facing
death is not the same man he was before the crisis came
upon him. Few can say 'I know how you feel', because few
have returned from the valley of the shadow and know how
he feels. No one can even say with full understanding, 'I
know him.' For he is, in a manner of speaking, not himself.
He may be better or he may be worse than his usual self,
but he is not the same. So a new relationship must be
established, starting with the patient, where he is in his own
thinking. The dying man's frame of mind must determine
the path to take, not the clergyman's."[43]

The priest is guided in his ministry by the Book of
Common Prayer's Office of Visitation of the Sick, although
he will have to adapt his methods of approach to meet
the particular spiritual needs of each individual patient.
There will be some who are already familiar with the
sacramental ministry of the Church, and here the priest's
ministry will be direct and devotional. There will be others
who are nominal members of the Church, to whom his
approach might seem vague and dubious. A few will have
already succumbed to the state of unconsciousness or will be
in a heavily drugged state before he arrives.

The Prayer Book Office instructs him to do three things:
1. To lead the patient to *penitence*. "To examine the sick
person whether he repent him truly of his sins, and be in
charity with all the world; exhorting him to forgive, from
the bottom of his heart, all persons that have offended him;
and if he have offended any other, to ask them forgiveness;

and where he hath done injury or wrong to any man, that he make amends to the uttermost of his power." 2. To help the patient exercise *charity*. "And if he have not before disposed of his goods, let him then be admonished to make his Will, and to declare his debts, what he oweth, and what is owing unto him; for the better discharging of his conscience, and the quietness of his Executors. But men should often be put in remembrance to take order for the settling of their temporal estates whilst they are in health." 3. To increase the patient's *faith*. "The minister shall rehearse the Articles of the Faith." Discreet and pertinent questions can be asked the sufferer—e.g., "You do believe that God is your Father, don't you?" "And that he loves you and has died for you?" "He now wants to receive you unto himself?" "You are not alone for he is always with you, and will never forsake you.... You do believe all this?" The priest will encourage the dying patient to lean on his faith and the faith of the whole Church, and assure him that he is being surrounded by love and prayer.

There is one last thing I would draw from the Divine models before me [stated Dean Vaughan in a sermon preached at St Edmund's, Salisbury, 1875] and that is, the Pastoral Office in its companionship of the dying.... People ... expect you at their deathbed. Expect, it may be, too much of you. Expect a miracle. Expect a "viaticum", a passport, and a safeguard, which lie not with man. Still they recognize that part of your Pastoral Office which I have called the companionship of the dying. How great, how solemn, how awful an undertaking! To accompany to the very brink of that dark river a dying man, to whom all is necessarily strange ... to guide the steps of the soul towards that plunge into the invisible; to point out to the alarmed, or (much, much worse) to the stupefied, a way of salvation never sought in life; or, on the other hand—blessed be God, it is sometimes so—to be permitted to go up, hand in hand with a believing and a rejoicing spirit, to the very threshold of the golden gates, and almost to look in after it as it enters—"who is sufficient for these things?" ... What earnestness should we feel, not to be found

helplessly silent or shamefully formal in the necessary suggestions of last words, last consolations, last prayers, to the
dying! What manner of persons, I repeat it, ought we Pastors
to be—were it but for this cause—in all holy conversation
and godliness.[44]

The priest can lead the practising churchman by means
of acts of faith and prayer to offer himself wholly into the
hands of his Heavenly Father. Ideally the patient should
make his peace with God and receive the Viaticum. The
priest will direct his attention more and more upon God
and his love and forgiveness, as extreme weakness will
probably make it difficult for the patient to make any con-
centrated effort to say his own prayers. Affirmations or short
arrowhead ejaculatory prayers are all helpful for the dying
to repeat slowly with the priest. Simple reassurances can be
whispered in the ear, for hearing is the last of the senses to
be lost. This is why all who minister to the patient have to
be careful what is said.

THE LAST SACRAMENTS

It is the feeling of guilt perhaps more than any other one
thing that seems to separate the dying from those around
them and make them feel lonely and abandoned.

THE SACRAMENT OF PENANCE

We have already noted how the Book of Common Prayer
exhorts the priest to "examine [the sick] whether he repent
him truly of his sins . . ." If it is found necessary to instruct
the dying (as indeed often is the case) about the significance
of penitence, the following questions will probably be
found helpful, dependent naturally on the particular circumstances—"Have you thought much about God?" "How
much do you really love him, do you think?" "Have you
said your prayers regularly, I wonder?" "Is there anything
in your life for which you would like to be forgiven?"
"Have you forgiven everyone you would wish?" "Is there

any particular sin about which you are worried at this time?"

The patient's confession can now be heard and he may be moved to contrition. If he has not been instructed formerly, the patient will have to be prompted by the priest who might use a simple form of question based, for example, on the Ten Commandments, to which the patient need answer only "yes", or "no", "sometimes", or "often". In some instances it will not be possible to insist on a formal confession, and a sincere desire for forgiveness will have to suffice. Where privacy is difficult, such as in a large hospital ward, the priest can sit very near to the bed and speak distinctly but quietly into the patient's ear. During the confession the penitent can either squeeze the priest's hand in response to questioning, tap a finger, or nod his head when a particular sin is confessed. In this way secrecy is assured, and less physical effort is involved for the patient who is already weak and languid. Where necessary the act of contrition can be made by the priest himself and then absolution given. Penance naturally will be something easily completed. The more familiar the better, as, for example, the Lord's Prayer or a well-known collect. If the penitent is getting weaker, the priest can say with him a short exhortation or ejaculatory prayer—"Jesus mercy": "O Lamb of God, that taketh away the sins of the world."

THE SACRAMENT OF HOLY COMMUNION

The last receiving of the *Holy Communion* is normally called the *Viaticum*—the provision for the way. Where swallowing is still possible and there is no risk of choking, the priest can administer either with a small portion of the intincted Host, or perhaps more often in species of wine alone from a spoon. If the patient is unable to speak, the priest will naturally make the appropriate responses for him, and shorten the service accordingly. If the members of the family are present they will be able to join and receive the sacrament together. Where possible this would ideally take place on the day of death. The rule of fasting is of course relaxed.

If there are difficulties in swallowing, or if for some reason the patient is totally unable to receive, he can be shown how to make a spiritual Communion, thereby uniting himself spiritually to the altar of God. The rubric in the Book of Common Prayer plainly states that

> If a man, either by reason of extremity of sickness, or for want of warning in due time to the Curate, or for lack of company to receive with, or by any other just impediment, do not receive the Sacrament of Christ's Body and Blood, the Curate shall instruct him, that if he do truly repent him of his sins, and steadfastly believe that Jesus Christ hath suffered death upon the Cross for him, and shed his Blood for his redemption, earnestly remembering the benefits he hath thereby, and giving him hearty thanks therefore he doth eat and drink the Body and Blood of our Saviour Jesus Christ profitably to his soul's health, although he do not receive the Sacrament with his mouth.

THE SACRAMENT OF HOLY UNCTION

When death is near, the Sacrament of *Holy Unction* can be viewed as the Last Anointing. Here again it is helpful if the family can be present so that both priest and sufferer can be uplifted in prayer. By the use of this sacrament the soul is prepared and strengthened for its entry into glory. Where the Holy Communion has been seen as the Viaticum, both Confession and Holy Unction will precede it. They can all be administered together if circumstances allow; otherwise they are used separately.

Almighty God is not confined or tied to the sacraments, and where it has not been at all possible for the dying to receive them, we should still believe that spiritual grace has been bestowed if the patient has been living a good life. The priest should pray that his soul might be brought to forgiveness and

From the perils of dying;
From any complying
With sin, or denying
His God, or relying
On self at the last,
From all that is evil,
From the power of the devil,
Thy servant deliver,
For once and for ever.[45]

When the body weakens, the patient's perception of physical sensations becomes blurred and indistinct, so that verbal communication proves difficult. In his description of the death of Prince Andrei Bolkinsky, in *War and Peace*, Leo Tolstoy vividly pictures this for us. He tells us that "Prince Andrei not only knew he was going to die but felt that he was dying, that he was already half dead. He felt remote from everything earthly and was conscious of a strange and joyous lightness in his being. Neither impatient nor anxious, he awaited what lay before him. That sinister, eternal, unknown and distant something which he had sensed throughout his life was now close upon him and—as he knew by the strange lightness of being that he experienced—almost comprehensive and tangible."[46]

Symbolic acts can now be used with much effectiveness and significance. A crucifix may be placed in the patient's hand, helping him to identify his pain and anguish with our Lord's, to be hallowed by his. "Hold Thou Thy Cross before my closing eyes". A religious picture can be held before him on which he can periodically concentrate his thoughts as far as he is able. In the *Life of Lacordaire* we read how in his extreme weakness he said, pointing to the crucifix, "I cannot pray, but I can look at him."

Verses of familiar hymns—"Abide with me", "How sweet the name of Jesus sounds", "O Jesus I have promised", etc.— and the repetition of the Holy Name, all help the patient to realize the presence of God. "Thou O Lord art in the midst of us, and we are called by Thy Name. Leave us not, O

Lord our God." By such acts the sufferer is made ready to
surrender himself to God's love and care. "I wait for the
breath of God, for God's breath", Von Hügel said gaily
when he knew he was dying. "Perhaps he will call me to-day
—tonight. Don't let us be niggardly toward God. He is
never a niggard toward us. . . . Let us try to be generous and
accept. . . . I would like to finish my book [i.e. his Gifford
Lectures]—but if not, I shall live it out in the Beyond."[47]

With the lapsed, the approach of the priest will of necessity
be somewhat different. If time and opportunity allow, the
patient can be gently and gradually reintroduced to the
faith, and if possible to repentance. One cannot hope to
instruct a patient adequately in a very limited period of
time, but he can be led to the four great verities of the
Christian faith. Here again quite simple questions framed
in such a way that the answer is "yes", can be asked about
belief in God, the Father, Son, and Holy Spirit; and about
Jesus Christ, the Son of God made Man, who died upon the
cross to save us from our sins, and by his resurrection opened
the gates of the Kingdom of God to all those who believe in
him. The priest should make sure that the patient is bap-
tized, and establish whether or not he has been confirmed.
Naturally no one should be coerced to accept spiritual
ministrations, and Eissler is wise to point out the danger of
"the last-minute attempts of some church representatives to
win dying patients over to the side of their brand of
dogma."[48]

One of the most practical problems facing the priest is
lack of time, for we are reminded by Jeremy Taylor that "to
dress a soul for a funeral is not a work to be dispatched at
one meeting". If he is not summoned until the very end, the
priest has to be very direct, committing the dying to the love
of God, assuring him that he is not alone. The "Our Father"
can be recited (together if possible), and short affirmations
offered—"Father, into thy hands I commend my spirit". If
time allows, the patient can receive Holy Communion and
Holy Unction.

7

In such an intimate ministry, the priest's own spiritual life will be tested to the full. As he attempts to share in the fears, the sufferings, and the loneliness of the dying, he will soon realize the full justification of the question, "Which is really harder, to die or to witness death?" Every parish priest, if he is to bring a meaningful ministry to the bedside, will mark well these words of Archbishop Anthony Bloom (op. cit).

> Simply being with the dying: hours together saying nothing: this is an ability which I dare say clergy should develop more than they possess it: the ability to sit with someone, saying or doing nothing. Not just sitting looking vaguely and vacantly about, just knowing that "if I sit for half-an-hour I will have done my job": and not sitting with a sort of pious look—"I am praying next to my patient": and not talking in a pious or impious way ... this ability, just to sit and go deep, so deep in sympathy, in compassion, is showing that you do not need these discourses, that your presence speaks: that if there is a need, you can put a hand on the person and it will mean more than whatever you can say.

Death is an entirely different thing to the very young, and mention must be made of our ministry to the dying child. At an early age death is often seen as a sleep, and what seems to disturb the child most is the thought of separation. Normally there is more dependence, and regression, and finally "an unrelated state". The priest will often find that the truth is far more acceptable to the young than any deceitful approach. The child's simple faith and trustfulness will help him meet death peacefully. Young children who have reached the age of reason can be led to simple confession and receive the Viaticum. Holy Unction, too, can be administered at the discretion of the priest.

Again, children's hymns—"Loving Shepherd of thy sheep", "Jesus, friend of little children", "There is a green hill far away"—and religious pictures (which must be well chosen, avoiding sentimentality) all help them to put their trust and confidence in their heavenly Father who loves them so much. If in early teaching the young have been led to see death as a natural part of life, they will be the more prepared to accept it when it draws near. The priest will dispel any thoughts and ideas which the child might foster that he is being punished for "being naughty", or that God is deliberately taking him away from "Mummy" and "Daddy" because of something he has done. The Gospel stories about Jesus' ministry and his great love for children will be read, so that Jesus is seen as a friend (Matt. 19.13–15; Mark 10.13–16, and Luke 18.15–17). For children, too, symbolic acts are important—the holding of the child's hand, the forming of the sign of the Cross in blessing, and the touch of the Laying on of Hands.

The ministry to the parents should always form part of our total ministry to the child, and ideally the relationship should be established before the terminal stage is reached. Their anxieties and attitudes to death can quickly be transmitted to the open and receptive mind of the child. Unwarranted reassurances and false promises must be avoided at all costs, for "excess of hope is presumption and leads to disaster. Deficiency of hope is despair and leads to decay" (Menninger).

PRAYERS OF COMMENDATION

This is the final provision which the Church has made for preparation for death. For a child the priest might use one of the following:

a. Holy Father, into thy loving care we commit the soul of this dear child. May thy holy angel bear him/her hence to behold the vision of thy Face. Grant him/her peace and joy in the protection of thine everlasting arms: for Jesus Christ's sake. Amen.

b. Dear Lord, who art calling this little one to thee: In thy great mercy hasten the coming of thy Holy Angel, that he/she may speedily be delivered from his/her suffering. Teach those who love him/her to say, "Thy Will be done". Out of the deep we cry unto thee. O Lord, hear our prayer, and let our cry come unto thee. Amen.

For an adult we have the following Prayer of Commendation, the final blessing of the departing soul:

Go forth, O Christian soul, out of this world, in the Name of God the Father Almighty who created thee; in the Name of Jesus Christ, the Son of the Living God, who suffered for thee; in the Name of the Holy Ghost who hast sanctified thee. In communion with the blessed Saints, and aided by Angels and Archangels, and all the armies of the heavenly host. May thy portion this day be in peace, and thy dwelling in the heavenly Jerusalem.

Upheld by faith in Christ and the ministry of the sacraments, the patient's terror and despair can be dispersed, and anxiety and loneliness eased. The soul is prepared for better things, as we pray that the dying may take to themselves the words of de Chardin—"When the ill that is to diminish me or carry me off strikes from without or is born in me . . . and above all at that last moment when I feel I am losing hold of myself and am absolutely passive within the hands of the great unknown forces that have formed me: in all these dark moments, O God, grant that I may understand it is You (provided only my faith is strong enough) who are painfully parting the fibres of my being in order to . . . bear me away within Yourself."[49]

Appendix

1

In the discussion concerning the spiritual care of patients between Matron's office staff and a floor administrator, which took place before the move to the Princess Margaret Hospital, Swindon, the subject of the "concealment trolley" was mentioned. The words of the Matron are significant and it is hoped that her suggestion will be followed not only in the new hospitals being built, but also in the existing ones:

> FLOOR ADMINISTRATOR: I have heard that there are trolleys used in many Regions so that, when the deceased patient is taken from the ward, the trolley is covered with a sheet and it looks like an ordinary trolley coming from the ward and no one knows a patient has died. Are we planning to have these?

> MATRON: No. I know what you mean, they are called conceal-ment trolleys. I think it is wrong to try to conceal the fact that a body is being transported. Naturally, the route to the mortuary will be the quietest and most private way; we shall not use the public corridor; but if nurses or other staff see the mortuary trolley coming along and it is clearly marked with a pall, I would expect them to stand aside and keep silent until the body has passed, showing respect for the dead. If a con-cealment trolley is used in the way it is intended, no one will know and laughter and loud talking will possibly go on. We must face facts and help other people to face up to them too.

> *Nursing Times: 4 December 1964*

2

Another feature is that of moving the dying patient into a small side-ward or to another part of the ward. In a recent report on *Human Relations and Hospital Care* by Ann Cartwright (Routledge & Kegan Paul, 1964) in Chapter V, p. 50, "Patients and Privacy", we read the following:

> When a patient dies this is clearly depressing for the other patients. The event is not only distressing in itself; it casts a gloom over the Ward, and can awaken patients' fear of death for themselves. In this century, and in our modern society with small families, death has become an increasingly unfamiliar event and a subject generally regarded as unmentionable. [A patient comments] "Especially when they are dying, we rarely had a day pass without somebody pass out. They used to move them up to sister's end. I hoped they wouldn't move me up there". [The writer continues] Although removal to a side ward may alleviate some of the distress, it does not dispel it all, and, of course, it may increase the apprehension of the

patient who is moved ... even when death does not occur on the ward, patients may learn about it and find concealment more fearful than disclosure. [Another patient's comments are then noted] "There was an 18-year-old girl who didn't come out of the anaesthetic. They told us in the ward that she had moved to another part of the hospital. I don't think those things should be kept in the dark. I think it would be better to be told."

3. THE NURSE'S DILEMMA

REFLECTIONS OF A THIRD YEAR STUDENT NURSE

... When I was a junior nurse the problem began to emerge, but there was no time to dwell upon it too much. No mention of such a problem was made in the Training School, and I was left to discover and face this problem by myself. I try to think of my patients as individuals and intelligent human beings, and to say the very least it goes very much against the grain to face a person who places great trust in me and not be able to answer his question honestly.

It is comparatively easy for the Consultant to say that a patient is not to be told of his incurable condition, and that apparently he must die in a few weeks or months. The Consultant is often remote, and sees his patients only for a few minutes each week. He is accompanied on his round by a small army of people, and this often helps to save him the embarrassment of being asked the awkward question. If the patient does pluck up sufficient courage to ask the Consultant or one of the doctors, his question may be ignored completely, passed off with a shrug, or answered by a stream of technical jargon, which means nothing to the patient, and often does more harm than good.

It is the nurse who comes into the closest contact with the patient, and she receives the confidences. Inevitably the sixty-four thousand dollar question comes—"Am I going to die?" ... If the patient is not very intelligent it may be possible to persuade him that he will get better and go home— if the nurse is successful in doing this I am told that she is a good nurse! But patients come in all sorts and sizes and I.Q.'s, and sometimes the sensible patient sees right through the fairy story we make up to answer his simple question—if he didn't already know the answer one look at my face would be quite sufficient anyway! Or perhaps he has already tried it on another nurse, and is seeing what tale I can cook up.

If the nurse is "successful" the patient may cease to worry —"Nurse says I shall be all right." . . . I believe too from my observations that at some time before death a person knows full well that he is dying, even if he hasn't realized it fully before. Again, it must come as a shock that the trusted nurse has been stringing him along—with a bit more warning how many things might have been put right in the time available! It grieves me to think that I am a party to the conspiracy and deception which has deprived the patient of this precious time. . . .

PART TWO

Litanies, Prayers,
and Hymns

Let every man by the labour of his mind and help of prayer, enforce himself in all tribulation and affliction, labour, pain and travail, without spot of pride or ascribing any praise to himself, to conceive a delight and pleasure in such spiritual exercise, and thereby to rise in the love of our Lord, with an hope of heaven, contempt of the world, and longing to be with God.   ST THOMAS MORE

When the ministers of religion are come, first let them do their ordinary offices, that is, pray for grace to the sick man for patience, for resignation, for health (if it seems good to God in order to his great ends). For that is one of the ends of the advice of the apostle. And therefore the minister is to be sent for not while the case is desperate, but before the sickness is come to its crisis or period. Let him discourse concerning the causes of sickness . . . let him call upon him to set his soul in order; to trim his lamp; to dress his soul; to renew acts of grace by way of prayer; to make amends in all the evils he hath done; and to supply all the defects of duty as much as his past condition requires, and his present can admit.   JEREMY TAYLOR

Soul of Christ, sanctify me.
Body of Christ, save me.
Blood of Christ, inebriate me.
Water from the side of Christ, wash me.
Passion of Christ, strengthen me.
O good Jesu, hear me.
Within thy wounds hide me,
Suffer me not to be separated from thee.
From the malicious enemy defend me,
In the hour of my death call me,
And bid me come to thee,
That with thy Saints I may praise thee,
For ever and ever. Amen.

The Lord is near; have no anxiety, but in everything make your requests known to God in prayer and petition with thanksgiving. Then the peace of God, which is beyond our utmost understanding, will keep guard over your hearts and your thoughts, in Christ Jesus.

Philippians 4.6–8. N.E.B.

Litany for One in Great Danger

O God the Father of Heaven;
Have mercy on the soul of thy servant.

O God the Son, Redeemer of the world;
Have mercy on the soul of thy servant.

O God the Holy Ghost, the Comforter;
Have mercy on the soul of thy servant.

O holy, blessed, and glorious Trinity, One God;
Have mercy on his soul.

Be merciful; blot out all *his* iniquities, O Lord.
Be merciful; defend and deliver *his* soul, O Lord.

From all dark and disbelieving thoughts; from all snares and temptations of the devil; and from all distrust of thine infinite love and mercy;
Defend and deliver his soul, O Lord.

From all agony and distress of mind or body; from all clinging to this vain world; and from all excessive fears of dying;
Defend and deliver his soul, O Lord.

By the infinite merits of thy sacred Passion; by the pangs of thy crucifixion; by thine unknown weight of agony; and by thy giving up of thy spirit into thy Father's hands;
Defend and deliver his soul, O Lord.

By the Burial of thy sacred Body in the Tomb; by the passing of thy blessed Spirit into the abode of the dead; and by thy preaching to the spirits in prison;
Defend and deliver his soul, O Lord.

By thy glorious Resurrection on the third day; by the rolling away of the stone from the grave; by thy victory over death; and by thy leading captivity captive;
Defend and deliver his soul, O Lord.

By thy glorious Ascension to the right hand of God; by thy parting blessing to thine Apostles; and by the promise of thy perpetual presence;

Defend and deliver his soul, O Lord.

By thy sending of the Holy Ghost the Comforter; by thine all-prevailing Intercession; by thy preparing the heavenly mansions for thy redeemed; and by thy coming to receive them unto thyself;

Defend and deliver his soul, O Lord.

In all time of agony and distress; in all time of faintness and dimness of faith; in all hours of fear and darkness; in all moments of weakness and helplessness of mind and body;

Defend and deliver his soul, O Lord.

In the last moments of this painful life below; in the awful parting of soul and body; in the hour of death; and in the day of judgement;

Defend and deliver his soul, O Lord.

Son of God, we beseech thee to hear us.
O Lamb of God, that takest away the sins of the world;

Grant him thy peace.

O Lamb of God, that takest away the sins of the world;

Have mercy upon him.

O Christ hear us.

Lord, have mercy upon *him.*
Christ have mercy upon him.
Lord, have mercy upon *him.*

Our Father ... etc.

Commendation and blessing, to be said by the Priest, standing.

The Almighty Lord, who is a most strong tower to all them that put their trust in him, to whom all things in heaven, in earth, and under the earth, do bow and obey, be now and evermore thy defence; and make you know and feel that there is none other Name under heaven given to man, in whom, and through whom, you may receive health and salvation, but only the Name of our Lord Jesus Christ. *Amen.*

and after that shall say,

Unto God's gracious mercy and protection we commit you. The Lord bless you and keep you. The Lord make his face to shine upon you, and be gracious unto you. The Lord lift up his countenance upon you, and give you peace, now and evermore.
Amen.

Litany for One Unconscious

O God the Father, who lovest us, have mercy upon us and hear our intercession.

O God the Son, who diedst for us, have mercy upon us and hear our intercession.

O God the Holy Ghost who helpest us, have mercy upon us and hear our intercession.

O holy, blessed and glorious Trinity, One God, have mercy upon us and hear our intercession.

Remember not, Lord, the offences of thy servant; neither take thou vengeance of *his* sins; spare *him*, good Lord, spare thy servant, whom thou hast redeemed with thy most precious Blood, and be not angry with *him* for ever.
Spare him, good Lord.

By thy all-prevailing Cross and Passion; by thy most sacred body which suffered upon Calvary; by the shedding of thy most precious Blood;
Good Lord, deliver him.

By the awful hiding of thy Father's face; by thy exceeding bitter cry; and by the bowing of thy head in death;
Good Lord, deliver him.

We sinners do beseech thee to hear us, O Lord God; and that it may please thee to grant to thy servant pardon for all *his* sins that they may not be remembered against *him*;
We beseech thee to hear us, good Lord.

That it may please thee, if thou seest fit, to restore *him* again to consciousness, and to enable *him* to call upon thee in *his* hour of need;

    We beseech thee to hear us, good Lord.

That it may please thee to grant unto *him* a peaceful and painless end, and all such blessings as in our ignorance we know not how to ask;

    We beseech thee to hear us, good Lord.

That it may please thee to bestow upon thy servant, the mercy thou shewdst to the dying thief, when thou saidst, "To-day thou shalt be with me in Paradise";

    We beseech thee to hear us, good Lord.

That it may please thee, above all, to grant unto *him* a blessed rest among thy saints departed; a glorious resurrection at the last day; and an eternal inheritance in thy kingdom;

    We beseech thee to hear us, good Lord.

Son of God.... etc.
(to conclude as previous Litany)

    (Litanies from *Pastor in Parochia*, How.).

Litany for the Dying

Lord have mercy upon us.
  Christ have mercy upon us.
Lord have mercy upon us.

V. Christ, hear us.
R. Christ, graciously hear us.

God the Father of heaven,
Have mercy upon thy servant.

God the Son, Redeemer of the world,
Have mercy upon thy servant.

God the Holy Ghost,
Have mercy upon thy servant.

Holy Trinity, One God,
Have mercy upon thy servant.

Jesu, by thy manifold and great mercies,
Have mercy upon him.

Jesu, by thy Agony and Bloody Sweat,
Have mercy upon him.

Jesu, by thy Strong Crying and Tears,
Have mercy upon him.

Jesu, by thy Cross and Passion,
Have mercy upon him.

Jesu, by thy Resurrection and Ascension,
Have mercy upon him.

Jesu, by thy Intercession and Mediation,
Have mercy upon him.

Jesu, for the Glory of thy Name,
Have mercy upon him.

Jesu, for thy Mercy's sake,
Have mercy upon him.

Jesu, for thy Truth's sake,
Have mercy upon him.

Jesu, for thy own sake,
Have mercy upon him.

From oppression and distress,
Good Lord, deliver him.

From excess of pain,
Good Lord, deliver him.

From thy Wrath,
Good Lord, deliver him.

From the burden of *his* sins,
Good Lord, deliver him.

From the terrors of conscience,
Good Lord, deliver him.

From impatience, distrust, or despair,
Good Lord, deliver him.

From any suffering that draws *his* mind from thee,
Good Lord, deliver him.

In this *his* last and greatest need,
Good Lord, deliver him.

From the assaults of the devil,
Good Lord, deliver him.

From the powers of darkness,
Good Lord, deliver him.

From the gates of hell,
Good Lord, deliver him.

In the hour of death and in the Day of Judgement,
Good Lord, deliver him.

We sinners beseech thee to hear us,
That it may please thee to remember *him* with the favour thou
bearest unto thy people,
> *We beseech thee to hear us.*

That it may please thee to visit *him* with thy salvation.
> *We beseech thee to hear us.*

That it may please thee to deliver *him* from the enemy,
> *We beseech thee to hear us.*

That it may please thee to forgive *his* sins, negligences, and
ignorances,
> *We beseech thee to hear us.*

That it may please thee to forgive what in the lust of the flesh,
and the pride of life *he* may have committed against thee,
> *We beseech thee to hear us.*

That it may please thee to forgive what in vain thoughts, or an
angry spirit *he* may have committed against thee,
> *We beseech thee to hear us.*

That it may please thee to forgive what in idle words, or un-
guarded speech *he* may have committed against thee.
> *We beseech thee to hear us.*

That it may please thee to make *him* a partaker of thy mercies in Christ Jesus,
We beseech thee to hear us.

That it may please thee to grant *his* soul joy and immortality with all thy saints,
We beseech thee to hear us.

That it may please thee to grant *his* body rest and a part in the resurrection of the Blessed,
We beseech thee to hear us.

V. Lamb of God, that takest away the sins of the world,
R. Have mercy upon *him*.

V. Lamb of God, that takest away the sins of the world,
R. Grant *him* thy peace.

V. Lord, have mercy upon *him*.
R. Christ, have mercy upon *him*.
V. Lord, have mercy upon *him*.

V. O Lord, deal not with *him* after *his* sins;
R. Neither reward *him* according to *his* iniquities.

V. As thou hast delivered thy saints from all fears and torments,
R. So save and deliver *him*.

Let us pray.

O Lord Jesus Christ, who hast said, I have loved thee with an everlasting love: We beseech thee in that same love to deliver the soul of thy servant (*N.*) from all pains and suffering, that through the gate of life *he* may enter in to rejoice with thy saints in glory everlasting; through thy merits, who livest and reignest with the Father, in the unity of the Holy Ghost, God for ever and ever. *Amen.*

THE BLESSING

The Passion of our Lord Jesus Christ bring us all to the joys of everlasting life. *Amen.*

Litany for the Dead

Lord, have mercy upon us.
Christ, have mercy upon us.
Lord, have mercy upon us.

O God the Father, Creator of the world,
Have mercy on the souls of the faithful departed.

O God the Son, Redeemer of mankind,
Deliver the souls of the faithful departed.

O God the Holy Ghost, Perfecter of the elect,
Give rest to the souls of the faithful departed.

Be merciful, O Lord;
And pardon their sins.

Be merciful, O Lord;
And hear our prayers.

By thy love, which has always compassion for the frailties of human nature,
Deliver them, O Lord.

By the infinite merits of thy Precious Blood,
Deliver them, O Lord.

By thy Cross and Passion,
Deliver them, O Lord.

By thy glorious Resurrection, when thou openedst the Kingdom of Heaven to all believers,
Deliver them, O Lord.

By thy triumphal Ascension into Heaven to prepare a place for thy servants,
Deliver them, O Lord.

By thy coming to judge the world, when the works of all shall be tried,
>*Deliver them, O Lord.*

We sinners beseech thee to hear us;

That the blessed vision of Jesus may comfort them and the glorious light of his Cross shine upon them;
>*We beseech thee to hear us.*

O Lamb of God, who wilt come with glory to judge the living and the dead,
>*Give rest to the souls of the faithful departed.*

O Lamb of God, at whose presence the earth shall be moved and the heavens melt away,
>*Give rest to the souls of the faithful departed.*

O Lamb of God, in whose blessed book of life all their names are written,
>*Give rest to the souls of the faithful departed.*

V. Deliver us, O Lord, in that dreadful day;
R. And place us with the Blessed at thy right hand for ever.

V. Lord hear my prayer;
R. And let my crying come unto thee.

Let us pray.

Almighty God, we commend to thee the souls of the faithful departed, that being dead to the world they may live with thee. Clothe them with excellent glory in thy Kingdom, and join them to the just and righteous who fulfil thy will in the City that is above. Grant them eternal rest, thou Lord of Mercy and Love! *Amen.*

(Litanies from *Handmaids of The Sick*, Faith Press 1929.)

A Little Office
for Laying-out the Dead

Grant them, O Lord, eternal rest, and let light perpetual shine upon them.

Lord, have mercy upon us.
Christ, have mercy upon us.
Lord, have mercy upon us.

Our Father....

De Profundis. Ps. 130

Let us pray.

O Lord Jesus Christ, whose most sacred Body holy men wrapped in fine linen and decked with sweet spices: Be present with us, we most humbly beseech thee, and enable us reverently to prepare the body of this thy servant, in trust that through the power of thy Resurrection it may hereafter be raised again, and being reunited with his soul may live with thee in glory. *Amen.*

AFTER THE BODY HAS BEEN LAID OUT

O Lord, to thy gracious care we commit this body which thou hast redeemed with thy most precious Blood; beseeching thee that as it is now sown a natural body it may hereafter be raised a spiritual body, through thy power, who died and was buried and rose again for us, and now livest and reignest with the Father and the Holy Ghost, God for ever and ever. *Amen.*

V. O Saviour of the world, who by thy Cross and precious Blood hast redeemed us,
R. Save us and help us, we humbly beseech thee, O Lord.

O God, in whose tender mercy the souls of the faithful departed are at rest: Of thy favour grant unto the soul of this thy servant (N.) pardon of all *his* sins and everlasting peace. *Amen.*

May the souls of the faithful departed, through the mercy of God, rest in peace. *Amen.*

(From *Handmaids of The Sick*, ibid.)

A Commendation for the Dying

O Good Shepherd, who gavest thy Life for the sheep, we commit into thy merciful hands the spirit and soul of this thy servant. Let not the shedding of thine own blood be in vain for *him*. Wash away the stains of *his* past sins, let thy love be with *him* even now; and when he passeth through the valley of the shadow of death receive *him* into the arms of thy mercy, into the blessed rest of everlasting peace. *Amen.*

O Blessed Jesu, whose soul was exceeding sorrowful even unto death; comfort the soul of thy servant in this hour of *his* greatest need. *Amen.*

O Blessed Jesu, who didst suffer a cruel and shameful death upon the Cross; support thy servant in the hour of *his* death. *Amen.*

O Blessed Jesu, whose sacred Body rose again the third day from the dead; raise thy servant in the glorious Resurrection of the just. *Amen.*

By thine Agony and Bloody Sweat, by thy Cross and Passion, by thy precious Death and Burial, by thy glorious Resurrection and Ascension, and by the coming of the Holy Ghost;
Good Lord, deliver him.

In all time of pain and anguish of mind and body; in all assaults of the enemy; in all deep waters of suffering; in the hour of death and in the day of judgement;
Good Lord, deliver him.

IN THE FINAL HOUR

God the Father, who hath created thee, bless thee;
God the Son, who hath redeemed thee, bless thee;
God the Holy Ghost, who hath poured down his Grace upon
thee, bless thee;
The Holy Trinity be now and evermore thy defence, assist thee
in this thy last trial, and bring thee into the way of everlasting
life. *Amen.*

Jesus Christ, who redeemed thee with his Agony and Death,
have mercy upon thee and strengthen thee in this final hour.

O Thou Lamb of God, that takest away the sins of the world,
grant *him* peace. *Amen.*

WHEN THE SOUL HAS DEPARTED

O Lord, the God of spirits and of all flesh, who didst put death
under thy feet, didst destroy the power of the devil, and gavest
thy life for the world: Grant thy mercy to the soul now before
thy Judgement Seat and in thy great love for sinners pardon
every sin committed by *him* in thought, word, and deed and in
neglect of thee, who art the Resurrection and the Life, and
who livest and reignest, God for evermore. *Amen.*

O God, to whom all things do live: Mercifully look upon the
soul of thy faithful servant, and grant that *he* may be purified
from all stain of sin, and entering into thy rest may pass from
glory to glory till *he* come to the full light of the Beatific Vision;
to which we beseech thee to bring us also of thine infinite
mercy; through Jesus Christ our Lord. *Amen.*

(From *Handmaids of the Sick*, ibid.)

Prayers for the Dying

O Lord Jesus, we beseech thee by the anguish of thy soul when thou didst hang upon the Cross, to have mercy on (*N.*) and all others who are near to death. Grant that *they* may omit nothing that is necessary to make *their* peace with thee, and that, cleansed from all *their* sins by thy Blood, *they* may enter into the joy of thy presence, who livest and reignest for ever and ever. *Amen.*

O Lord, look down from heaven; behold, visit, and sustain this thy servant. Look upon *him* with the eyes of thy mercy, give *him* comfort and sure confidence in thee, defend *him* from the danger of the enemy, and keep *him* in perpetual peace and safety, for Jesus Christ's sake. *Amen.*

FOR A DYING CHILD

O Lord Jesus Christ, who didst take little children into thine arms and bless them: Bless, we beseech thee, this thy child; take *him* into the arms of thine everlasting mercy, keep *him* from all fear and terror, and bring *him* into the company of those who behold thy face for ever. *Amen.*

O Gracious Father, whose love is greater than the love of earthly fathers: Have mercy upon thy little child, and in all *his* pain and sickness support and comfort *him* and make *him* to lie still in thine everlasting arms; through Jesus Christ our Lord. *Amen.*
(From *Handmaids of the Sick,* ibid.)

FOR A GOOD DEATH

O eternal Father, I beseech thee, of thy boundless mercy, and by the life and passion of thy dear Son, enable me to persevere to the end, and to die in thy grace.

O blessed Jesus, by the love of thine eternal Father and by thy last words upon the Cross whereby thou didst commend thy spirit into his hands, I pray thee to receive my soul at my last hour.

O Holy Spirit, true God, have mercy upon me and guard me with thy holy inspirations now and in the hour of my death.

O most Holy Trinity, One God, have mercy upon me now, and in the hour of death, and in the day of judgement. Amen.
                    (From *My Day with Jesus*, Mirfield Publications.)

FOR ONE UNCONSCIOUS

O merciful Lord Jesus, by the merits of thy Cross and Passion, hear us on behalf of this thy servant, who through weakness of mind and body cannot now plead for *him*self. Mercifully regard *his* infirmity, pardon all *his* sins, and bring *him* to everlasting joy; who livest and reignest . . .
                    (From *Handmaids of The Sick*.)

FOR DEPARTED SOULS

Rest eternal grant to them, O Lord; and may everlasting light shine upon them.

O God, the Creator and Redeemer of all them that believe, grant unto the souls of thy servants departed the remission of all their sins; that through devout prayers they may obtain the pardon they have always desired. *Amen.*

O God, whose nature and property is ever to have mercy and to forgive: Look favourably on the souls of the faithful departed, and grant them remission of all their sins; that, being loosed from the bands of death, they may attain unto life eternal, through Jesus Christ our Lord. *Amen.*

Absolve, we beseech thee, O Lord, the souls of thy servants departed, that though dead unto the world, they may live with thee; and those sins which through the frailty of the flesh they have committed in their earthly life, do thou of thy great mercy wash away; through Jesus Christ our Saviour, who liveth and reigneth with thee in the unity of the Holy Spirit, One God, world without end. *Amen*.

(*My Day with Jesus*, ibid.)

O God, the King of Saints, we praise and magnify thy holy Name for all thy servants who have finished their course in thy faith and fear; for the Blessed Virgin Mary, for the holy Patriarchs, Prophets, Apostles, and Martyrs, and for all other of thy righteous servants; and we beseech thee that, encouraged by their example, strengthened by their fellowship, and aided by their prayers, we may attain unto everlasting life; through the merits of thy Son, Jesus Christ our Lord. *Amen*.

O Father of all, we pray to thee for those we love, but see no longer. Grant them thy peace; let light perpetual shine upon them; and in thy loving wisdom and almighty power work in them the good purpose of thy perfect will; through Jesus Christ our Lord. *Amen*.

FOR AN ANNIVERSARY OF ONE DEPARTED

Almighty God, we remember this day before thee thy faithful servant (*N*.), and we pray that, having opened to *him* the gates of larger life, thou wilt receive *him* more and more into thy joyful service; that *he* may win with thee and thy servants everywhere, the eternal victory; through Jesus Christ our Lord. *Amen*.

FOR THOSE WHO MOURN

O Heavenly Father, whose blessed Son Jesus Christ did weep at the grave of Lazarus his friend: Look, we beseech thee, with compassion upon those who are now in sorrow and affliction; comfort them, O Lord, with thy gracious consolations; make them to know that all things work together for good to them that love thee; and grant them evermore sure trust and confidence in thy fatherly care; through the same Jesus Christ our Lord. *Amen*.

(From *For Those who Mourn*, S.P.C.K.)

O thou, who at the grave of Lazarus didst mourn the ravages of death, tenderly comfort these thy children who sorrow for their dead.

O thou, who only hast the keys of death and of the grave, open upon those who are in its shadow of bereavement, the entrance of thy heavenly light.

O thou, who didst go to prepare a place for thine own, make the separation of this death blessed upon both sides with an undying love.

O thou, who art the Beginning and the End, enable us to trust thee for renewal, unceasingly, of this sacred gift, which thou hast withdrawn.

O thou, who art our everlasting life, vouchsafe to everyone saddened by death the joys of the sacrifice, communion, and commemoration of the altar; that its continual bond may keep us one, eternally, in thee, who art the Resurrection and the Life, and who livest and reignest with the Father and the Holy Ghost, one God, world without end. *Amen.*

(From E. A. L. Clarke, *The People's Missal.*)

Hymns

1 ABIDE with me; fast falls the eventide;
The darkness deepens; Lord, with me abide!
When other helpers fail, and comforts flee,
Help of the helpless, O abide with me.

2 Swift to its close ebbs out life's little day;
Earth's joys grow dim, its glories pass away;
Change and decay in all around I see;
O thou who changest not, abide with me.

3 I need thy presence every passing hour;
What but thy grace can foil the tempter's power?
Who like thyself my guide and stay can be?
Through cloud and sunshine, O abide with me.

4 I fear no foe with thee at hand to bless;
Ills have no weight, and tears no bitterness.
Where is death's sting? where, grave, thy victory?
I triumph still, if thou abide with me.

5. Hold thou thy Cross before my closing eyes;
Shine through the gloom, and point me to the skies:
Heaven's morning breaks, and earth's vain shadows flee;
In life, in death, O Lord, abide with me!

H. F. LYTE, 1793–1847.

1 JESU, Lover of my soul,
    Let me to thy bosom fly,
While the nearer waters roll,
    While the tempest still is high:
Hide me, O my Saviour, hide,
    Till the storm of life is past;
Safe into the haven guide,
    O receive my soul at last.

2 Other refuge have I none;
    Hangs my helpless soul on thee;
Leave, ah! leave me not alone,
    Still support and comfort me.
All my trust on thee is stayed,
    All my help from thee I bring;
Cover my defenceless head
    With the shadow of thy wing.

3* Thou, O Christ, art all I want;
    More than all in thee I find:
Raise the fallen, cheer the faint,
    Heal the sick, and lead the blind.
Just and holy is thy name;
    I am all unrighteousness;
False and full of sin I am,
    Thou art full of truth and grace.

4. Plenteous grace with thee is found,
    Grace to cover all my sin;
Let the healing streams abound;
    Make and keep me pure within.
Thou of life the fountain art;
    Freely let me take of thee;
Spring thou up within my heart,
    Rise to all eternity.

C. WESLEY, 1707–88.

1 JUST as I am, without one plea
   But that thy Blood was shed for me,
   And that thou bidd'st me come to thee,
      O Lamb of God, I come.

2 Just as I am, though tossed about
   With many a conflict, many a doubt,
   Fightings within, and fears without,
      O Lamb of God, I come.

3 Just as I am, poor, wretched, blind;
   Sight, riches, healing of the mind,
   Yea all I need, in thee to find,
      O Lamb of God, I come.

4 Just as I am, thou wilt receive,
   Wilt welcome, pardon, cleanse, relieve:
   Because thy promise I believe,
      O Lamb of God, I come.

5 Just as I am (thy love unknown
   Has broken every barrier down),
   Now to be thine, yea, thine alone,
      O Lamb of God, I come.

6. Just as I am, of that free love
   The breadth, length, depth, and height to prove,
   Here for a season, then above,
      O Lamb of God, I come.

CHARLOTTE ELLIOT, 1789–1871.

1 HOW sweet the name of Jesus sounds
   In a believer's ear!
It soothes his sorrows, heals his wounds,
   And drives away his fear.

2 It makes the wounded spirit whole,
   And calms the troubled breast;
'Tis manna to the hungry soul,
   And to the weary rest.

3 Dear name! the rock on which I build
   My shield and hiding-place,
My never-failing treasury filled
   With boundless stores of grace.

4 Jesus! my Shepherd, Husband, Friend,
   My Prophet, Priest, and King,
My Lord, my Life, my Way, my End,
   Accept the praise I bring.

5 Weak is the effort of my heart,
   And cold my warmest thought;
But when I see thee as thou art,
   I'll praise thee as I ought.

6. Till then I would thy love proclaim
   With every fleeting breath;
And may the music of thy name
   Refresh my soul in death.

J. NEWTON, 1725-1807.

1 MY God, how wonderful thou art,
   Thy majesty how bright,
How beautiful thy mercy-seat,
   In depths of burning light!

2 How dread are thine eternal years,
   O everlasting Lord,
By prostrate spirits day and night
   Incessantly adored!

3 How wonderful, how beautiful,
   The sight of thee must be,
Thine endless wisdom, boundless power.
   And awful purity!

4 O, how I fear thee, living God,
   With deepest, tenderest fears,
And worship thee with trembling hope,
   And penitential tears!

5 Yet I may love thee too, O Lord,
   Almighty as thou art,
For thou hast stooped to ask of me
   The love of my poor heart.

6 No earthly father loves like thee,
   No mother, e'er so mild,
Bears and forbears as thou hast done
   With me thy sinful child.

7. Father of Jesus, love's reward,
   What rapture will it be
Prostrate before thy throne to lie,
   And gaze and gaze on thee.

F. W. FABER, 1814-63.

1 NEARER, my God, to thee,
        Nearer to thee!
E'en though it be a cross
        That raiseth me:
Still all my song would be,
'Nearer, my God, to thee,—
        Nearer to thee!'

2 Though, like the wanderer,
        The sun gone down,
Darkness be over me,
        My rest a stone;
Yet in my dreams I'd be
Nearer, my God, to thee,
        Nearer to thee!

3. There let the way appear,
        Steps unto heaven;
All that thou send'st to me
        In mercy given.
Angels to beckon me
Nearer, my God, to thee,
        Nearer to thee!

                    SARAH F. ADAMS, 1805–48.

1 ROCK of ages, cleft for me,
  Let me hide myself in thee;
  Let the Water and the Blood,
  From thy riven side which flowed,
  Be of sin the double cure,
  Cleanse me from its guilt and power.

2* Not the labours of my hands
  Can fulfil thy law's demands;
  Could my zeal no respite know,
  Could my tears for ever flow,
  All for sin could not atone;
  Thou must save, and thou alone.

3 Nothing in my hand I bring,
  Simply to thy Cross I cling;
  Naked, come to thee for dress;
  Helpless, look to thee for grace;
  Foul, I to the Fountain fly;
  Wash me, Saviour, or I die.

4. While I draw this fleeting breath,
  When mine eyes are closed in death,
  When I soar through tracts unknown,
  See thee on thy judgement throne;
  Rock of ages, cleft for me,
  Let me hide myself in thee.

                              A. M. TOPLADY, 1740-78.

1 THE King of love my Shepherd is,
   Whose goodness faileth never;
I nothing lack if I am his
   And he is mine for ever.

2 Where streams of living water flow
   My ransomed soul he leadeth,
And where the verdant pastures grow
   With food celestial feedeth.

3 Perverse and foolish oft I strayed,
   But yet in love he sought me,
And on his shoulder gently laid,
   And home, rejoicing, brought me.

4 In death's dark vale I fear no ill
   With thee, dear Lord, beside me;
Thy rod and staff my comfort still,
   Thy Cross before to guide me.

5 Thou spread'st a table in my sight;
   Thy unction grace bestoweth:
And O what transport of delight
   From thy pure chalice floweth!

6. And so through all the length of days
   Thy goodness faileth never;
Good Shepherd, may I sing thy praise
   Within thy house for ever.

SIR H. W. BAKER, 1821–77.

1 I HEARD the voice of Jesus say,
   'Come unto me and rest;
Lay down, thou weary one, lay down
   Thy head upon my breast:'
I came to Jesus as I was,
   Weary, and worn, and sad;
I found in him a resting-place,
   And he has made me glad.

2 I heard the voice of Jesus say,
   'Behold, I freely give
The living water, thirsty one;
   Stoop down, and drink, and live:'
I came to Jesus, and I drank
   Of that life-giving stream;
My thirst was quenched, my soul revived,
   And now I live in him.

3. I heard the voice of Jesus say,
   'I am this dark world's Light;
Look unto me, thy morn shall rise,
   And all thy day be bright:'
I looked to Jesus, and I found
   In him my Star, my Sun;
And in that light of life I'll walk
   Till travelling days are done.

H. BONAR, 1808–89.

1 THERE is a green hill far away,
   Without a city wall,
 Where the dear Lord was crucified
   Who died to save us all.

2 We may not know, we cannot tell,
   What pains he had to bear,
 But we believe it was for us
   He hung and suffered there.

3* He died that we might be forgiven,
   He died to make us good;
 That we might go at last to heaven,
   Saved by his precious Blood.

4* There was no other good enough
   To pay the price of sin;
 He only could unlock the gate
   Of heaven, and let us in.

5. O, dearly, dearly has he loved,
   And we must love him too,
 And trust in his redeeming Blood,
   And try his works to do.

MRS C. F. ALEXANDER, 1823–95.

1 LOVING Shepherd of thy sheep,
  Keep thy lamb, in safety keep;
  Nothing can thy power withstand,
  None can pluck me from thy hand.

2* Loving Saviour, thou didst give
  Thine own life that we might live;
  And the hands outstretched to bless
  Bear the cruel nails' impress.

3 I would bless thee every day,
  Gladly all thy will obey,
  Like thy blessèd ones above,
  Happy in thy precious love.

4 Loving Shepherd, ever near,
  Teach thy lamb thy voice to hear;
  Suffer not my steps to stray
  From the straight and narrow way.

5. Where thou leadest I would go,
  Walking in thy steps below,
  Till before my Father's throne
  I shall know as I am known.

JANE E. LEESON, 1807–82.

Bibliography

Notes

Indexes

Bibliography

BOOKS

Alvarez, W. C. *Nervousness, Indigestion and Pain*. Constable 1923.

A. M. W. *The Threshold: Reflections on Death*. Constable 1923.

Andrew, Fr. *Soul's Discipleship*. Mowbray 1936.

Andrewes, Lancelot. *A Manual for the Sick*. Rivington 1869.

Anthony, Sylvia. *The Child's Discovery of Death*. Kegan Paul 1940.

Arnold, Edwin. *Death and Afterwards*. New Amsterdam 1847.

Ayre, John (ed.). *Sick Man's Salve: Becon*. Parker Soc. Cambridge 1844.

Bacon, Francis. *Essays*. J. M. Dent 1955.

Baxter, Richard. *The Reformed Pastor*. S.C.M. 1956.

Bayly, Lewis. *The Practise of Pietie*. Hamilton, Adams 1612.

Beauvoir, Simone de. *A Very Easy Death*. Deutsch and Weidenfeld and Nicolson 1966.

Bell, F. W. *The Great Adventure*. Johannesburg 1946.

Bonnar, A. *The Catholic Doctor*. Burns and Oates 1945.

Boros, Ladislaus. *The Moment of Truth*. Burns and Oates 1965.

Boyle, Robert. *Occasional Reflections upon Several Subjects*. London 1665.

Brauer and others. *Approach to Terminal Illness*. Nat. Cancer Found. Inc.

Browne, Sir Thomas. *Religio Medici*. C.U.P. 1955.

Cabot, R. C. and Dicks, R. L. *The Art of Ministering to the Sick*. Macmillan 1938.

Campbell, W. E. (ed.). *The English Works of Sir Thomas More*. 1931.

Chardin, Teilhard de. *Le Milieu Divin*. Collins 1960.

—— *The Making of a Mind*. Collins 1961.

Clark, Cecil. *How to face Death*. Faith Press 1958.

Clarke, W. K. Lowther. *Death and After*. S.P.C.K.: Chichester Pamphlets 1957.

Comper, F. M. M. *The Book of the Craft of Dying*. London 1917.

Coverdale, Miles. *Treatise on Death*. Parkers Soc. 1846.

Cox, J. E. (ed.). *A Priest's Work in Hospital*. S.P.C.K. 1955.

Crafer, T. W. (ed.). *A Priest's Vade Mecum*. S.P.C.K. 1945.

Diggle, J. W. *Death and After Life*. Williams & Northgate 1918.

Donne, John. *Complete Poetry & Selected Prose*. Nonesuch 1962.

Dorczynski, A. *The Man they wouldn't let Die*. Secker & Warburg 1966.

Drelincourt, Charles. *The Christian's Consolations against the Fears of Death*. J. Wallis, London 1701.

Eaves, A. *The Mastery of Death*. Wellby 1906.

Edmunds, V. and Scorer, C. G. (eds.). *Ideals in Medicine*. Tyndale 1958.

Eissler, K. R. *The Psychiatrist and the Dying Patient*. Intern. Univ. 1955.

Feifel, H. (ed.). *The Meaning of Death*. McGraw Hill 1959.

Fletcher, J. *Morals and Medicine*. Princeton 1954.

Flood, Dom. Peter. *New Problems in Medical Ethics*. Mercier 1962.

Fortune, D. *Through the Gates of Death*. Aquarian 1957.

Francis, D. N. *Good News about Death*. Epworth 1958.

Frankl, Viktor. *Man's Search for Meaning*. H. & S. 1963.

—— *The Doctor and the Soul*. Knopf 1952.

Fulton, Robert (ed.). *Death and Identity*. John Wiley 1965.

Gage, G. J. *Ministering to Persons*. Epworth 1966.

G.A.P. *Death and Dying: Attitudes of Patient and Doctor*. Mental Health Materials Center 1965.

Gavey, C. J. *The Management of the Hopeless Case*. H. K. Lewis 1952.

Gliddon, C. P. and Powell, M. *Called to Serve*. H. & S. 1952.

Greenstock, D. L. *Death: The Glorious Adventure*. Burns & Oates 1956.

Guntrip, H. (ed.). *Facing Life & Death*. Allen & Unwin 1959.

Hackel, Sergei. *One, of Great Price*. Darton, Longman & Todd 1965.

Hammarskjöld, Dag. *Markings*. Faber 1964.

Harton, Sybil. *On Growing Old*. H. & S. 1957.

Herbin, Pierre. *We Die Unto the Lord*. Challoner 1960.

Hiltner, Seward. *Pastoral Counseling*. Abingdon-Cokesbury 1949.

Hobhouse, Stephen. *A Discourse on The Life to Come*. Independent 1954.

Hocking, W. E. *The Meaning of Immortality in Human Experience*. Harper 1957.

Holmes, Eveline. *There is a Country*. S.P.C.K. 1962.

Hopkinson, A. W. *The Gate of Life*. Mowbrays 1937.

Horstmann, Karl (ed.). *Library of Early Christian Writers*. Sonnenschein 1895.

Huddleston, T. (ed.). *Dying We Live*. Fontana. 3rd imp. 1962.

Hughes, H. L. G. *Peace at The Last*. Gulbenkian Fnd. 1960.

Jenkins, Daniel (ed.). *The Doctor's Profession*. S.C.M. 1949.

Jenkins, David. *Parson at Work*. H. & S. 1966.

Johnson, Paul. *Pastoral Ministration*. Nisbet 1955.

Kelly, Gerald, s.j. *Medico-Moral Problems*. Clonmore 1960.

Kettlewell, John. *Death Made Comfortable*. London 1695.

Klinger, Kurt. *A Pope Laughs*. Fontana 1966.

Lewis, C. S. *Letters to Malcolm*. Bles 1964.

—— *The Problem of Pain*. Bles 1940.

Liddon, H. P. *Advent Sermons*. Longmans Gr. 1899.

Mackenna, R. W. *The Adventure of Death*. John Murray 1931.

Maurice, F. D. *Theological Essays*. James Clarke 1957.

Mercer, J. E. *Why Do We Die?* Kegan Paul 1919.

Moorman, J. R. H. *St Francis of Assisi*. S.P.C.K. Seraph 1963.

Moran, Lord. *The Anatomy of Courage*. Constable 1945.

Ogilvie, Heneage. *No Miracle among Friends*. Max Parrish 1959.

Orwell, George. *Shooting an Elephant & Other Essays*. Secker & Warburg 1950.

Osler, W. *Science & Immortality*. Houghton, Mufflin 1904.

Pelgrin, M. *And A Time to Die*. Routledge & Kegan Paul 1961.

Perkins, Wm. *The Whole Treatise of Cases of Conscience*. London 1602.

Pike, James. *Beyond Anxiety*. Scribner's 1953.

Pole, K. F. M. *Handbook for the Catholic Nurse*. Robert Hale 1964.

Rahner, Karl. *The Theology of Death*. Burns and Oates 1964.

Reindorp, Alix and George. *Death and Those we Love*. Mothers' Un. 1963.

Reynolds, A. G. *Life and Death*. Lutterworth 1960.

Ross, J. D. *Margaret*. H. & S. 1963.

Rylands. *The Ars Moriendi*. London 1881.

Saunders, Cicely. *The Care of the Dying*. Nursing Times Reprint.

Scherzer, Carl. *Ministering to the Dying*. Prentice-Hall 1964.

Schlemmer, Andre. *Faith & Medicine*. Tyndale Press 1957.

Sheen, Fulton. *Peace of Soul*. Blandford 1955.

Simcox, C. E. *Is Death the End?* S.P.C.K. Seraph 1960.

Smyth, Patterson. *The Gospel of the Hereafter*. H. & S. 1912.

Soutar, W. *Diaries of a Dying Man*. Chambers 1954.

Southard, Samuel. *Religion and Nursing*. Broadman 1959.

Stanbrook, Benedictine of. *To Any Christian*. Burns & Oates 1964.

Standard and Nathan (eds.). *Should The Patient know The Truth?* Springer, N.Y. 1955.

Steere, D. V. (ed.). *Spiritual Counsels and Letters of Baron Friedrich von Hugel*. Darton, Longman & Todd 1964.

Stengel. *Suicide and Attempted Suicide*. Penguin 1964.

Stevas, St John. *The Right to Life*. Hodder 1963.

Talbot, E. K. *Retreat Addresses*. S.P.C.K. 1955.

Taylor, Jeremy. *Holy Living: Holy Dying*. Longmans Green 1941.

Tillich, Paul. *The Courage to Be*. Fontana 1962.

Tournier, Paul. *A Doctor's Casebook in the Light of the Bible*. S.C.M. 1962.

—— *The Seasons of Life*. S.C.M. 1964.

Treves, F. *The Elephant Man & Other Reminiscences*. Cassell 1923.

Vann, Gerald. *The Divine Pity*. Sheed & Ward 1946.

Vinet, A. *Pastoral Theology*. Edinburgh 1855.

Walker, Kenneth. *The Circle of Life*. Jonathan Cape 1942.

—— *Patients and Doctors*. Penguin 1957.

Walpole, G. H. S. *The Gospel of Hope*. Scott 1914.

—— *Waiting: Thoughts on Death*. Wells Gardner 1925.

Walton, Izaac. *Lives of Donne etc.* Nonesuch 1929.

Warren, Max. *Interpreting the Cross*. S.C.M. 1966.

Weatherhead, L. *Why do Men Suffer?* S.C.M. 1935.

Wertenbaker, Lael. *Death of a Man*. Heinemann 1957.

Westberg, Granger. *Minister and Doctor Meet*. Harper 1961.

Williams, H. *The Four Last Things*. Mowbray 1960.

Williams, Charles. *Descent into Hell*. Faber 1937.

Wilson, D. M. *Triumph over Fear*. Gollancz 1966.

Worcester, Alfred. *The Care of the Aged, the Dying and the Dead*. C. C. Thomas, Springfield Ill. 1935.

Wyon, O. *The Grace of the Passion*. S.C.M. 1959.

Young, Richard. *The Pastor's Hospital Ministry*. Broadman 1959.

ARTICLES

Aldrich, C. K. "The Dying Patient's Grief", *Journal of the American Medical Association*, Vol. 184, 1963, pp. 329–31.

Ashbrook, J. B. "The Lost Dimension of the Physical", *Pastoral Psychology*, Vol. 17, No. 161, 1966.

Baker, J. M. and Sorensen, K. C. "A Patient's Concern with Death", *American Journal of Nursing*, Vol. 63, 1963, pp. 90–2.

Barber, Hugh. "The Act of Dying", *Practitioner*, Vol. 161, 1948.

Beatty, D. C. "Shall we talk about Death?" *Pastoral Psychology*, VI, February 1955, pp. 11–14.

Bergh, R. L. V. "Let's Talk about Death", *American Journal of Nursing*, Vol. 66, No. 1, pp. 71f.

Bluestone, H. and McGahee, C. L. "Reactions to Extreme Stress: Impending Death by Execution", *American Journal of Psychiatry*, Vol. 119, 1962, pp. 393–6.

Booth, Gotthard. "The Cancer Patient and the Minister", *Pastoral Psychology*, Vol. 17, No. 161, 1966.

Boyling, D. "Ministering to the Dying," Church of England Hospital Chaplain's Conference, Oxford, July 1960.

Brauer, Paul. "Should the Patient be told the truth?" *Nursing Outlook*, Vol. 8, 1960.

Bromberg, W. and Schilder, P. "Death and Dying", *Psychoanalytic Review*, Vol. 20, 1933, pp. 133–85.

Cappon, D. "The Dying", *Psychiatric Quarterly*, Vol. 33, July 1959.

Chadwick, M. "Notes upon Fear of Death", *International Journal of Psychoanalysis*, 10, 1929, pp. 321–34.

Chapman, Earle. "He was in the prime of life", *Journal of Pastoral Care*, Vol. XIV, No. 2, Summer 1960.

Crouch, M. "Incurable Disease: The Real Problem", *In The Service of Medicine*, No. 14, July 1958.

Davidson, R. P. "To Give Care in Terminal Illness", *American Journal of Nursing*, Vol. 66. No. 1.

Davis, Charles, "Death and Worldly Holiness", *New Christian*, Vol. 3, 1965.

Denniston, Robin, "Roll on Death", *Prism*, February 1962.

Dicks, Russell, "How Doctors Treat the Dying", *The Pastor*, November 1959.

Doctor, A. "The Patient, The Doctor and Death", *The Burrswood Herald*, Easter 1964.

Fairbanks, Rollin. "Ministering to The Dying", *Journal of Pastoral Care*, Fall 1948.

Feifel, Herman. "Older Persons Look at Death", *Geriatrics*, Vol. II, 1956, pp. 127–30.

—— "Attitudes of Mentally Ill Patients towards Death", *Journal of Nervous and Mental Disease*, Vol. 122, 1955, pp. 375–80.

Felix, R. H. "The Role of the Clergyman in Time of Crisis". Paper delivered at Conference on Pastoral Care, University of Florida, October 1963.

Fisher, Lord. "Should The Doctor tell?" *Guild of St Raphael Quarterly*, February 1960.

Fitch, J. A. "Preparation for Death", *Theology*, Vol LXVI, No. 521, November 1963.

Folck, M. M. and Nie, P. J. "Nursing Students Learn to face Death", *Nursing Outlook*, Vol. 7, 1959, p. 9.

Friedman, S. B. and others. "Behavioral Observations on Parents anticipating Death of a Child", *Pediatrics*, Vol. 32, 1964.

Gerle, B. and others. "The Patient with Inoperable Cancer from the Psychiatric and Social Standpoints. A Study of 101 Cases", *Cancer*, Vol. XIII, November 1960, pp. 1206–17.

Gibson, Paul. "The Dying Patient", *Guild of St Raphael Quarterly*, Vol. 4, No. 6, May 1961.

Gorer, G. "The Pornography of Death", *Encounter*, Vol. 5, 1958, pp. 49–52.

Grant, Ian. "Care of the Dying", *British Medical Journal*, 2, 1957, pp. 1539–40.

Hackett & Weisman. "The Treatment of the Dying", *Journal of Pastoral Care*, Vol. XVIII, No. 2, Summer 1964.

Hays. "The Night Neil Died", *Nursing Outlook*, Vol. 10, 1962 p. 12.

Hinton, H. M. "The Physical and Mental Distress of the Dying", *Quart. J. Med.*, 32, No. 1, 1963.

Horder, Lord. "Signs & Symptoms of Impending Death", *Practitioner*, Vol. 161, No. 962, August 1948.

Inglis, T. "Death on a Ward", *Nursing Outlook*, Vol. 12, No. 1, 1964, p. 28.

Kalish, R. A. "An Approach to the Study of Death Attitudes", *The American Behavioral Scientist*, Vol. VI, 1963, pp. 68–70.

—— "A Continuum of Subjectively Perceived Death", adapted from a paper presented at the annual meeting of the Gerontological Society, Los Angeles, 12 November 1965.

Kasley, V. "As Life Ebbs", *American Journal of Nursing*, March 1948, pp. 170–3.

Kelly, W. D. and Friesen, S. R. "Do Cancer Patients Want to be Told?", *Surgery*, Vol. 27, 1950, pp. 822–6.

Leak, W. N. "The Care of the Dying", *Practitioner*, Vol. 161, No. 962, August 1948.

Lehrman. "Reactions to Untimely Death", *Psychiatric Quarterly*, Vol. 30, October 1956.

Leslie, R. "Helping The Dying Patient and His Family", Paper read at 56th Annual Forum: National Conference on Social Welfare, San Francisco, May 1959.

Letourneau, Charles, "A Soliloquy on Death", *Hospital Management*, November 1963, pp. 58f.

Lloyd, G. A. L. "Should The Dying be Told?" *Guild of St Raphael Quarterly*, Vol. 3, No. 4, November 1959.

Lourie, R. S. "The Pediatrician and the Handling of Terminal Illness", *Pediatrics*, Vol. 32, 1963, pp. 477–9.

Marcel, Gabriel. "My Death and Myself", *Review of Existential Psychology and Psychiatry*, Vol. II, No. 2, May 1962.

Maurer, Adah, "Maturation of Concepts of Death", *British Journal of Medical Psychology*, Vol. 39, 1966, p. 35.

Menninger, Karl, "Hope", *American Journal of Psychiatry*, Vol. 116, 1959, pp. 481–91.

Morrissey, J. R. "A Note on Interviews with Children facing imminent Death", *Social Casework*, Vol. 44, No. 6, 1963.

Natterson, J. M. and Knudson, A. G. "Observations about Fear of Death in Fatally Ill Children and Their Mothers", *Psychosomatic Med.*, Vol. XXII, No. 6.

Ogilvie, H. "Journey's End", *Practitioner*, No. 179, 1957, pp. 584–591.
10

Oken, Donald, "What to Tell Cancer Patients", *Journal of American Medical Association*, Vol. 175, 1961, pp. 1120–8.

Perske, Robert, "Death and Ministry: Episode and Response", *Pastoral Psychology*, Vol. 15, 1964, pp. 25–35.

Platt, R. "Reflections on Ageing and Death", *Lancet*, 5 January 1963.

Quint, J. and Strauss, A. L. "Nursing Students, Assignments and Dying Patients", *Nursing Outlook*, Vol. 12, 1964, pp. 24–7.

Reeves, R. "A Study of Terminal Cancer Patients", *Journal of Pastoral Care*, Winter 1960.

Ristau, Ruth "The Loneliness of Death", *American Journal of Nursing*, Vol. 58, 1958, pp. 1283–4.

Rosenthal, Hattie. "Psychotherapy for The Dying", *American Journal of Psychotherapy*, Vol. XI, No. 3, 1957, pp. 626–33.

—— "The Fear of Death as an Indispensable Factor in Psychotherapy", *American Journal of Psychotherapy*, Vol. 17, 1963, pp. 619–30.

Rowley, Francis, s.j. "The Theology of Dying", *Guild of Catholic Psychiatrists Bulletin*, Vol. IX, No. 3, July 1962.

Ryle, J. A. "Of Death and Dying", *Lancet*, Vol. 2, 1940, pp. 401–2.

—— "Angor Animi", *Guy's Hospital Reports*, No. 99, 1950, pp. 230–5.

—— "The sense of dying", *Guy's Hospital Reports*, Vol. 99, 1950, pp. 204–29.

Saunders, C. "Terminal Illness", Paper read at Health Congress, Royal Society of Health, April 1961.

—— "Care of The Dying", Pfizer Lecture, South Eng. Scotland Faculty of Coll: of Gen. Pract., November 1962.

—— "Care of The Dying", *Union of St Luke*, Periodical Letter, No. 24.

—— "The last Stages of Life", *Nursing Times*, 30 July 1965.

—— "Watch with me", *Nursing Times*, 26 November 1965.

Schilder, P. "The Attitude of Murderers towards Death", *Journal of Abnormal and Social Psychology*, Vol. 31, 1936, pp. 348–63.

Schneiders, A. A. "The Psychology of Dying", *Bulletin of Guild of Catholic Psychiatrists*, Vol. X, No. 1, January 1963.

Shrut, Samuel D. "Attitudes toward Old Age and Death", *Mental Hygiene*, No. 42, 1958, pp. 259–66.

Small, N. "Should The Dying be told?" *Guild of St Raphael Quarterly*, February 1960.

Smith, A. N. Exton- "Terminal Illness in the Aged", *Lancet*, 1961, ii. 305.

Solnit, A. J. and Green, M. "Psychologic Considerations in the Management of Death on Pediatric Hospital Services", *Pediatrics*, Vol. 24, 1959, pp. 106–12.

Steen, J. W. "Hindrances to the Pastoral Care of the Dying", *Pastoral Psychology*, March 1958.

Stewart, J. M. "Parents take heart at City of Hope", *American Journal of Nursing*, October 1962, pp. 82–5.

Strauss, A. L., Glaser, B. and Quint, J. C. "The Nonaccountability of Terminal Care", *Hospitals*, Vol. 38, 1964, pp. 73–87.

Trowell, H. C. "The Necessity of a Philosophy to cover the Practice of Medicine", *Union of St Luke*, Periodical Letter, No. 28, October 1963.

Wahl, C. "The Physician's Management of Death and the Dying Patient", *Proceedings of 3rd World Congress of Psychiatry*, June 1961.

Weisman, A. D. and Hackett, T. P. "Predilection to Death", *Psychosomatic Medicine*, Vol. 23, 1961, pp. 232–56.

—— "The Dying Patient", *Forest Hospital Publications*, Vol. 1, 1962, pp. 16–21.

Williamson, J. B. "Sick Visiting: Care of the Chronic Sick and Dying", *For Health and Healing*, October 1964.

Zilboorg, G. "The Sense of Immortality", *Psychoanalytic Quarterly*, Vol. VII, 1938, pp. 171–99.

Decisions about Life and Death, Report published for The Church Assembly Board for Social Responsibility by the Church Information Office, 1965.

NOVELS

Agee, J. *Death in the Family*. Owen 1965.

Bennett, A. *Old Wives' Tales*. Everyman 1948.

Caldwell, Taylor. *The Man who Listens*. Collins 1961.

Camus, A. *The Plague*. Penguin 1948.

Cather, W. *Death Comes for the Archbishop*. Hamilton 1961.

Faulkner, W. *Intruder in the Dust*. Penguin 1957.
—— *As I Lay Dying*. Penguin 1963.
Gloag, J. *Our Mother's House*. Pan 1966.
Hemingway, E. *The Old Man and the Sea*. Cape 1952.
Hilton, J. *Goodbye Mr Chips*. Hodder 1959.
—— *Lost Horizon*. Pan 1947.
Huxley, A. *After Many a Summer*. Penguin 1948.
Lawrence, D. H. *Sons and Lovers*. Penguin 1956.
Mann, Thomas. *The Magic Mountain*. Penguin 1949.
Mansfield, K. *The Garden Party and Other Stories*. Penguin 1951.
McIlvanney, W. *Remedy is None*. Eyre & Spottiswoode 1966.
Minahan, J. *The Passing Strange*. Secker & Warburg 1966.
O'Connor, F. *Everything that Rises must Converge*. Faber & Faber 1966.
Post, L. van der. *Journey to the Interior*. Penguin 1957.
Spark, Muriel. *Memento Mori*. Penguin 1959.
Tolstoy, L. *The Death of Ivan Ilych and Other Stories*. New American Library 1960.
—— *War and Peace*. Dent 1957.
Trilling, L. *The Middle of the Journey*. Penguin 1963.
Vries, P. de. *The Blood of the Lamb*. Gollancz 1962.
Waugh, E. *The Loved One*. Penguin 1951.
Wells, H. G. *The History of Mr Polly*. Pan 1963.
Wilde, Oscar. *The Picture of Dorian Gray*. Penguin 1949.
Wilder, Thornton. *Bridge of San Luis Rey*. Penguin 1941.
Yonge, Charlotte. *The Heir of Redcliffe*. Macmillan 1901.

Notes to Part One

CHAPTER 1

1. *Advent in St Paul's*, Liddon, Sermon XLIX, Longmans, Green and Co., 1899.
2. In *The Crafte to Live Well and to Dye Well* of Wynkyn de Worde, workman and successor to Caxton (1505), over eighty such woodcuts were included.
3. Cf. Interrogations in "The Visitation of the Sick", Book of Common Prayer. The Creed is recited in an interrogatory manner so that "the sick person shall answer".
4. It is strange that throughout the whole work there is only a rather indirect reference to the ministry of the priest. This might possibly infer that, along with similar works, the book was written for those who were outside the priest's ministrations. Another theory is that, because of the rather frequent emergencies and sudden deaths, instructions were needed for the friends and families of the dying.
5. A similar work to Becon's was *The Last Battell of The Soule in Death*, by Zachary Boyd (1628). It is a most lengthy work and a rather exhausting discourse between a "sicke man", a "pastour", and a "carnall Friend".
6. *Thomas More*, Chambers; Jonathan Cape, 1935, p. 385.
7. *The English Works of Sir Thomas More*, ed. W. E. Campbell, Vol. 1, 1931, p. 77.
8. In the Second Apology of Justin Martyr we are told that objections were raised to private celebrations of Holy Communion at a very early period.
9. *Treatise on Death*, Miles Coverdale. Printed by Parker's Society, xxii, Cambridge, 1846.
10. *Lives of Donne etc.*, Izaak Walton; Library of the Old English Prose Writers, Vol. V, p. 45.
11. Ibid., p. 54.
12. *Complete Poetry and Selected Prose of John Donne, Dean of St Paul's*; Nonesuch Press, 1962, pp. 537–8.
13. Donne, Sermon XV; Whitehall, 29 February 1627–8.
14. *Devotions*, Vol. III, p. 510.

15. *The Christian's Consolations against the Fears of death.* . . . *directions for preparing him to die well,* Charles Drelincourt; London 1701.
16. *Saints Everlasting Rest,* Baxter; III.12.viii.

CHAPTER 2

1. Cf. "The ancient Romans had a certain tenderness and detestation of the name of death, they could not name death, no, not in their wills. There they could not say Si mori contigerit, but si quid humanitus contingat, not if, or when I die, but when the course of nature is accomplished upon me." Donne. Also *Churchyards,* John Betjeman:

> Oh why do people waste their breath
> Inventing dainty names for death?
> On the old tombstones of the past
> We do not read "At peace at last"
> But simply "died" or plain "departed".

2. 1,500 persons die each day in England and Wales. See appended table of deaths p. 39 above.
3. In a *Meeting Point* programme, entitled "The Problem of Pain" (B.B.C. Television, 11 August 1963), Archbishop Anthony Bloom remarked that "one of the things that impresses me in the Western attitude to death, is that it is almost indecent to die. One should do that on the quiet. . . . What I find so often is that people should have been taught about death when they were full of sap and life, and when they could still face death not as a terror but as a challenge."
4. *Thoughts for the Times on War and Death,* Freud; Hogarth, 1925, Vol. 4, p. 304.
5. *Is Death the End?,* Carroll E. Simcox; S.P.C.K. Seraph, 1960, p. 6. Cf. "In Articulo Mortis", Sir Frederick Treves, *The Elephant Man and Other Reminiscences*; Cassell and Co., 1930, 2nd imp., p. 199: "The dread of death is an instinct common to all humanity. Its counterpart is the instinct to self-preservation, the resolve to live." *The Courage To Be,* Paul Tillich; Nisbet and Co. Ltd., 1952, p. 39: "The anxiety of fate and death is most basic, most universal and inescapable."
6. *Bulletin of the Menninger Clinic,* C. W. Wahl; 22, 1958, pp. 214–223.
7. "In the Shadows", David Gray. *The Penguin Book of Sick Verse,* ed. George Macbeth, Penguin Books, 1963.
8. Cf. *Clio I,* Charles Peguy: "There is a residue of mystery in death, a centre, an abyss, a revelation of mystery—and quite in-

dependent of whose death, be it your father or your mother—
every man is gripped . . . the deafest hear, the blindest see, and
the closed are opened, and even those who are armoured in in-
sensibility bow their heads for a moment at a funeral."

9. *The Adventure of Death*, Robert W. Mackenna; John Murray,
London, 1931, p. 10.

10. We have a wonderful description of heaven from the pen of John
Bunyan: "Now, just as the gates were opened to let in the men, I
looked in after them, and behold the city shone as the sun: the
streets were paved with gold, and in them walked many men with
crowns on their heads . . . there were also of them that had wings,
and they answered one another without intermission, saying,
Holy, holy, holy is the Lord. And after that they shut up the
gates. *Which, when I had seen, I wished myself among them.*"

11. *Silex Scintillans*, Henry Vaughan.

12. Thomas Tryon (1634–1703).

13. *Advent Sermons*, op. cit p. 60.
In a letter written to his father by Mozart during the former's last
illness (4 April 1787), we read the following: "I never lie down in
my bed without reflecting that perhaps I (young as I am) shall
never see another day: yet none of all who know me can say that
I am socially melancholy or morose. For this blessing I daily thank
my Creator and wish it from my heart for all my fellow-men."
Quoted in *The Psychiatrist and the Dying Patient*, Eissler: International University Press, 1955, p. 99. A rubric in the ancient
Ritual of St Ouen of Rouen attempted to allay the loneliness of a
dying brother: "When they hear the signal [for the agony] all the
brethren run up, and though among us it is forbidden to run, in
this case all run, as if there were a fire: indeed it is an order. . . .
The whole community must run to the spot, for they must always
be present at the hour of death." Quoted in *The Last Rites*, J.-C.
Didier; Burns and Oates, 1961, p. 93.

14. "La mort du racheté"; R. Guelluy in *Revue diocésaine de
Tournai*, 1959, p. 89. Quoted in J.-C. Didier, op. cit., p. 19.

15. Cf. "I must leap alone, and no one can come with me; but in my
leaping I shall not be alone. Our Lord my Shepherd will be leading me, my guardian angel will be holding me, the Church on
earth will see me off across the river, and the Church Expectant
will receive me the other side." From *Meditations of a Caterpillar*,
A Religious of C.S.M.V., Faith Press, 1962, p. 84.

16. *Counseling the Dying*, Bowers, Jackson, Knight, and Leshan;
Nelson, 1964, p. 19.

17. *Religio Medici*, Thomas Browne; C.U.P., 1955, Part I, Sect. 38, p.
50.

18. "Death", *Encyclopedia of Religion and Ethics*.

19. *Occasional Reflections upon Severall Subjects*, Robert Boyle, London, 1665; Sect. II, p. xi. Cf. "When we must die, we are sorry for every unkind word we have said to someone who is so dear to us; if we could go on living, we should remember that and control ourselves much better." *Dying we live*, Fontana, 3rd imp. 1962, p. 191.

20. *The Diaries of a Dying Man*, William Souter; W. & R. Chambers Ltd., 1954, p. 177.

21. *The Adventure of Death*, Robert W. Mackenna; John Murray, London, 1931.

22. *Principia Therapeutica*, Methuen and Co. Quoted in *The Management of the Hopeless Case*, C. J. Gavey; H. K. Lewis and Co. Ltd, 1952, p. 2.

Cf. "When you feel that you are really at the foot of the wall (or the edge of the ditch, if you prefer) that is the time you feel apprehension—and you feel that only our Lord can give us true forgetfulness of self, sincere, deep and real.—The apprehension, I believe, is worse than the reality,—for all whom I have seen die, died so simply!" A letter written by Pierre Teilhard de Chardin when a soldier-priest from Verdun, 30 October 1916; *The Making of a Mind*: de Chardin; Collins, 1965, p. 137.

23. *The Elephant Man and Other Reminiscences*, Cassell and Co., 1923, pp. 199f.

24. "Dying men rarely experience pain or apprehension, or terror or remorse; their lives peter to an end, 'like their birth, their death is a sleep and a forgetting'." *The Anatomy of Courage*, Lord Moran; Constable, London 1945, Chapter XVI, pp. 154f.

25. Tizard in *Facing Life and Death*, ed. Guntrip; Allen and Unwin, 1959, p. 165.

26. One of the small group of persons present when Sir Winston Churchill died remarked, "The years fell away from his face, and he looked again the way that he looked during the war". Cf. *Religio Medici*: "Thus it is observed, that men sometimes, upon the hour of their departure, do speak and reason above themselves. For then the soul begins to be freed from the ligaments of the body, begins to reason like herself, and to discourse in a strain above mortality."

Wantage Poems, compiled by Sylvia Mary, c.s.m.v., 1965, p. 45, "The Faces of the Dead", Sister Isobel Everild:

> But I have seen upon the faces of the dead
> A look of radiant ecstasy,
> As if the spirit now released
> Had soared untrammelled up to God
> And left behind a token of His love.

27. *Science and Immortality*, Osler; Houghton, Mifflin and Co., Boston, 1906.
28. "Terminal Illness in the Aged", *Lancet*, 1961, ii.305.
29. "The Physical and Mental Distress of the Dying"; *Quarterly Journal of Medicine*, 1963, i.32.
30. "The Dying Patient", Paul C. Gibson; *Guild of St Raphael Quart.*, May 1961. See Appendix: correspondence in *The Times*, 1914, on the painlessness of death.
31. *Immortality*, Holmes; Oxford Library of Practical Theology, 1909, pp. 231f.
32. *The Moment of Truth*: Ladislaus Boros. Burns and Oates, 1965, p. 95.
33. *Dream of Gerontius*, Newman.
    Cf. the last words of:
    Louis XIV: "I thought that dying had been more difficult."
    Sir Philip Sidney: "I would not change my joy for the empire of the world."
    Beethoven: "I shall hear in heaven."
    Sir Walter Scott: "God bless you all! I feel myself again."
    Albert, Prince Consort: "I have such sweet thoughts."

    Letters written by prisoners in Germany on the verge of execution: *Dying We Live*, foreword by Trevor Huddleston, Fontana, 3rd imp., 1962:
    "I never knew that dying is so easy" (p. 58).
    "Death is not a fearful thing. It is the separation that is hard, and heavy to bear" (p. 59).
    "When one has really achieved complete surrender to the will of God, there is a marvellous feeling of peace and a sense of absolute security" (p. 88).

CHAPTER 3

1. "How Doctors treat the Dying", Russell Dicks; *The Pastor*, November 1959.
2. *Medical Tribune*, 8 May 1961.
3. *The Times*, 12 September 1959.
4. *Nervousness, Indigestion and Pain*, Walter C. Alvarez; Staples Press Ltd., 1956, p. 130.
5. *The Times*, 17 September 1959.
6. "Do Cancer Patients Want to be Told?" Kelly and Freisen; *Surgery*, Vol. 27, 1950, pp. 822–6.
7. "The Patient with Inoperable Cancer from the Psychiatric and Social Standpoints", *Cancer*, xiii, November 1960, pp. 1206–17.
8. *The Death of Ivan Ilych*; New American Library, 1960, pp. 137f.

9. *Saint Francis of Assisi*, J. R. H. Moorman; Seraph S.P.C.K., 1963, p. 113, Cf. The account of the last days of Bishop Chavasse, former Bishop of Rochester: "He [the doctor] assured her that the X-Ray had shown that cancer was rampant. Death could not be delayed beyond a few weeks or a couple of months at most. He asked were they to tell the Bishop. Mrs Chavasse was in no doubt at all. He must be told immediately. The doctor went up first and told him the facts of the case, clear and precise. The effect on the Bishop was astonishing. It was as though he had been told that in a short while he would be leaving for a dream holiday. A quarter of an hour after being told that he had but a short time to live, he had his wife searching through the 'Pilgrim's Progress' for the part where Christian and others were conscious of the summons of the celestial post: and of the beckoning of the Shining Ones seen by Christian at the last. . . ." *The Chavasse Twins*, Selwyn Gummer; Hodder and Stoughton, 1963, p. 223.

10. *Care of the Dying*, Dr Cicely Saunders, p. 20; Nursing Times Reprint.

11. Tizard in *Facing Life and Death*, ed. Guntrip; Allen and Unwin, 1959, p. 139.

12. *Death, Grief and Mourning in Contemporary Britain*, Cresset Press, 1965, p. 18.

13. "Often when I see a fine affectionate husband and wife trying to deceive each other after thirty years in which they have faced together every buffet of fortune, I say, 'Why don't you two share this sorrow also? You who have gone through all the great adventure of life hand in hand, surely you should be going through this one, the greatest of all, in the same way. As one of you now starts through the valley of the Shadow, why shouldn't the other be staying close? Why shouldn't you both be talking frankly about the future?'" (Walter Alvarez, op. cit., p. 133.)

14. "The Treatment of the Dying", T. P. Hackett and A. D. Weisman; *Journal of Pastoral Care*, Vol. XVIII, No. 2, Summer 1964.

15. "We believe that it is a mistake to assume that everyone feels the same unutterable fear of death. Furthermore we believe that it is almost impossible to withhold knowledge of death from a dying person, and that to attempt to do so blindly imposes an unintended exile on someone facing ultimate loneliness. . . . We do not mean that the physician must tell the patient bluntly that he has a fatal, incurable condition and will be done in within the month. Truth has many faces, each of which can be employed as it is needed . . ." (Hackett and Weisman, op. cit.).

16. "Should the Doctor Tell?" Lord Fisher of Lambeth; *Guild of St Raphael Quarterly*, Vol. 4, No. 1, February 1960, p. 6.

17. *Peace at the Last: A Survey of Terminal Care in the U.K.*, H. L. Glyn Hughes; London, 1960, p. 42.

18. See Hinton, op. cit., "If a patient sincerely wanted to know his possible fate, and was met by prevarication or empty reassurance, he felt lonely and mistrustful."

19. *The Journal of the Church of England Hospital Chaplains' Fellowship*, New Vol. I, No. 1, February 1965.

20. *The Meaning of Death*, ed. Herman Feifel; "Treatment of the Dying Person", Gerald J. Aronson; McGraw-Hill Book Co. Inc., 1959, pp. 252f.

21. *The Tempest.*

22. *Current Medical Abstracts for Practitioners*, "Care of the Dying", Vol. 3, No. 2, p. 82.

23. *Margaret*, James Davidson Ross; Hodder and Stoughton, 1963, pp. 58–9.

24. *Forum and Century* magazine, June 1939. Reprint pp. 7–8; quoted in "Helping the Dying Patient and his Family", a paper by the Reverend Robert C. Leslie, Associate Professor of Pastoral Psychology and Counselling at Pacific School of Religion, Berkeley, California.

25. *Patients and Doctors*, Pelican Books, 1957, p. 119.

26. "Signs and Symptoms of Impending Death", Lord Horder; *The Practitioner*, August 1948.

27. Winter 1960, pp. 218f.

28. *The Meaning of Death*, op. cit., p. 123.

29. *Retreat Addresses*, S.P.C.K., 1953, p. 184.

30. *The Practitioner*, August 1948.

31. "Reaction to Extreme Stress: Impending Death by Execution"; *American Journal of Psychiatry*, November 1962, pp. 393–6.

CHAPTER 4

1. *Care of the Aged, the Dying and the Dead*, Worcester; Springfield, Illinois, 1960.

2. Cf. the deathbed scene of Gerald Scales in *The Old Wives' Tale*, Arnold Bennett; Everyman Library, Dent, 1960, pp. 484f.

3. *The Penguin Book of Sick Verse*, p. 157.

4. See Appendix 1, 2 on pp. 88–90 above.

5. "The Psychology of Dying", Cappon; *Psychiatric Quarterly*, July 1959.

6. "A Doctor Looks at Death", Dr Felix Martilbanez; *Readers' Digest*, August 1964, p. 84.

7. *Devotions upon Emergent Occasions*, John Donne.

8. "Care of the Dying", Dr Cicely Saunders; *Current Medical Abstracts for Practitioners*, Vol. 3, No. 2.
9. *The Journal of the Church of England Hospital Chaplains' Fellowship*, New Vol. 1, No. 1, February 1965.
10. "Psychotherapy for the Dying", Hattie R. Rosenthal; *American Journal of Psychotherapy*, Vol. XI, No. 3, July 1957.
11. *Religion and Nursing*, Samuel Southard; Broadman Press, 1959.
12. *Guild of St Raphael Quarterly*, February 1960. Cf. "Apart from the relatives only two people have any right to be present when anyone sets out on that journey from which there is no return. One is the doctor to ensure that the departure is as comfortable as possible. The other is the padre to provide the spiritual solace that enlightens the darkness that precedes the hereafter." Leading article, *Medical News*, 11 September 1964.
13. Worcester, op. cit.
14. *New Problems in Medical Ethics*, ed. Dom Peter Flood; Mercier Press, No. 1, 1962, p. 120.
15. *Devotions upon Emergent Occasions*, John Donne, VI, p. 515.
16. Worcester, op. cit.
17. *The Psychiatrist and the Dying Patient*, Eissler; International Un. Press, 1955, p. 252.
18. *The Doctor and the Soul*, Viktor Frankl; Knopf, 1953, p. 133.
19. "The Dying Patient", Dr Paul Gibson; *The Practitioner*, 1961, Vol. 186, pp. 85–91.
20. *The Practitioner*, No. 179, 1957.
21. In his address to the Derby Diocesan Conference, 1962, the Bishop of Derby, Dr Geoffrey Allen, made the following observations on the ethical problems involved in the prolongation of life: "It may be possible with modern drugs to keep the body alive when the mind is in a state of coma, and when there seems no probability that consciousness can return. The prolongation of what is in fact a living death may be causing intense strain to relatives, themselves perhaps also in advancing years. What is the duty of a doctor under such circumstances? To withhold the drug which might prolong life seems too great a responsibility for any one individual to take alone. Yet if we have faith that beyond death there is waiting the everlasting mercy of the Creator, then it would seem that a time comes when it is right to accept the natural death of the body. There is here a very complex moral issue which requires consideration in all its different aspects, theological, ethical and medical, and in which those trained in these different fields need therefore to aid one another." Cf. also the philosophy of Stevenson's *Aes Triplex*: "Does not life go down with better grace, foaming in full body over a precipice, than miserably struggling to an end in sandy deltas?"

For a study of the moral issues involved, the reader is referred to:

Decisions about Life and Death, published for the Church Assembly Board for Social Responsibility by the Church Information Office, 1965.

Life, Death and the Law, Norman St John-Stevas; Eyre and Spottiswoode, 1961.

The Right to Life, Norman St John-Stevas; Hodder, 1963.

"Anti-Dysthanasia: The Problem of Prolonging Death", Reverend Joseph Fletcher; *The Journal of Pastoral Care,* Vol. XVIII, No. 2, Summer 1964.

22. *New Problems in Medical Ethics,* p. 122.

23. "Management of the Patient with Terminal Illness", P. S. Rhoads, *Journal of the American Medical Association,* Vol. 192, No. 8, 24 May 1965, pp. 661f.

24. A questionnaire sent by The Institute of Religion and Medicine to the Medical Schools in England and Wales, asking what was done about teaching students how to understand patients' religious attitudes, how to cope with the dying and with various ethical problems, and whether the chaplain took any part in teaching, received fourteen replies. Of these only three felt able to complete the questionnaire; one of these estimated that three hours, and one five hours, were spent in three years on these subjects; the third could not assess the time. The remaining eleven replied that there was no specific or regular teaching, nor apparently any agreed policy on them, but that they were left to individual consultants, and that students had opportunities for discussion. Some seemed confident that such opportunities were taken: more seemed to doubt whether this was so.

25. *No Miracle Among Friends,* Sir Heneage Ogilvie; Max Parrish, 1959.

26. "Becoming a Nurse," Aileen D. Ross; a sociologist's analysis of the preparation of professional nurses in Canadian hospitals.

27. Cf. "That eternal 'why?' . . . that question mark twisted like a fish-hook in the human heart. 'Let there be light', we cry, and only the dawn breaks." *The Blood of the Lamb,* Peter de Vries; Gollancz, 1963, p. 243.

28. See "The Nurse's Dilemma", Appendix, Chapter 4, pp. 90–91 above.

29. Since the above suggestions were made, a recent report, *Christianity and Nursing Today,* has been published by Epworth Press. The findings reported are from a working-party brought together by the Nurses' Christian Movement, and among the recommendations there is included the following: "When a dying patient says, 'Nurse, why did this happen to me?' or when a girl not out of her teens is told to nurse a baby dying of leukaemia; what she says and what she does and how she does it will be based upon several

things. It has been said that 'Preparation is the mother of spontaneity', and in part her answer to the question 'Why?' depends upon how far she has faced such a question herself previously. One thing is certain—to trot out *'the* answer' is useless. And her reaction to seeing a baby die slowly is again, in a sense, something that can only be prepared for indirectly. . . . The Chaplain's lectures in the Nurses' Training School need reconsideration . . . the most valuable seem to be almost informal, drawing out the nurses' own problems for discussion and answer."

30. *What about Nursing?* Joy Burden; S.P.C.K. 1959.

31. The actual nursing techniques used by the nurse in her care of the dying are naturally out of the scope of such a book as this. Suffice it to call the nurse's attention to words of Dr Glyn Hughes (*Peace at the Last*, Section 73, p. 41): "Whether it be in hospital, a nursing home or at home, the one requirement at the very end is a high standard of nursing."
   Helpful literature for nurses on the care of the dying patient:
   The Care of the Dying, Cicely Saunders; Nursing Times Reprint.
   Bedside Nursing: An Introduction, Darwin, Markham and Whyte; Heinemann (Chapter 22, pp. 193–200).
   Becoming a Nurse, Ross; Macmillan.

32. *Counseling the Dying*, Bowers, Jackson, Knight and LeShan; Nelson, 1964, p. 60.

33. The difficulties involved in communication between doctor, nurse, and family are illustrated in an article describing the visit of a student nurse to the family of a patient who had died in hospital. The nurse "was bewildered about how M's mother viewed the scene in the recovery room, and saw something quite different from that seen by the attending personnel. I now understand [she continues] that 'tunnel vision' brought about by great personal anxiety prevented her from listening to the explanation offered by the nurse. This illustrated clearly for me the fact that in explaining, as in teaching, it is important for the nurse to remember that an extremely anxious patient or relative may view a situation which is entirely strange to them quite differently from the nurse. What each person sees or comprehends will differ to some extent, but what the very anxious person sees or hears may be very different indeed. "The Death of a Young Man", Mary C. S. Googe; quoted with permission from the *American Journal of Nursing*, November 1964, p. 134.

34. *Le Milieu Divin*, Teilhard de Chardin, Collins, 1960, p. 61.

35. *Peace at the Last*, Section 88, p. 48.

36. "The Responsibility of Social Work in the care of the Cancer Patient", article by Ruth D. Abrams, Asst. Professor, Boston

University School of Social Work, and Supervisor, Massachusetts General Hospital.

37. *Door of Eternity*, Sybil Harton; Hodder and Stoughton, 1965, p. 141.
38. *Counseling the Dying*, p. 63.
39. "Management of the Patient with Terminal Illness", op. cit.
40. "The Psychology of Dying", op. cit.
41. See Chapter 1. Also, cf. Perkins' *Salue for a Sick Man*.
42. *New Problems in Medical Ethics*, p. 123.
43. "The Rôle of the Clergyman in Time of Crisis", Robert H. Felix; Conference on Pastoral Care, Florida, 22 October 1963.
44. *The Word of Life*, ed. R. R. Williams; S.P.C.K., 1960, pp. 101–2.
45. *Dream of Gerontius*, Newman.
46. *War and Peace*, Tolstoy; Penguin Books, Vol. II, p. 1162.
47. *Letters to a Niece*, Greene; London, Dent 1928, p. xlii.
48. *The Psychiatrist and the Dying Patient*, p. 119.
49. *Le Milieu Divin*.

Index of Subjects

Index of Authors, Books, and Journals